CHRONICLES OF A LOST BOY ON CHRISTMAS

FIRST EDITION

A.F. PRESSON

ASIN: B09JL1S9F8
ISBN: (Paperback) 978-1-7372433-3-5
ISBN: (Hardback) 978-1-7372433-4-2

Translations

Brud- *Grime or mud*
Prezent- *Present or gift*
Kasza- *Groats (Oats)/Porridge*
Sozzled- *Soused or inebriated*
Gabinet- *Private office*
Herbata- *Polish tea*
Gulasz- *Goulash/Stewed meat*
Karp- *Variation of carp (Freshwater fish)*
Swashbuckler- *Lunatic*
Nie- *No*
Dupa- *Buttocks*
Blimey- *Golly/Gee wiz*
Pierniki- *Spice Cookie*
Huhns- *Hens*
Knipp- *Sausage*
Brot- *Bread*
Magisfjell- *Magic Mountain*

The Miracle of Christmas Day

No brightly lit tree
No gifts or cries of joy,
Only the young hopeful gaze
Of an innocent boy.

Eyes full of wonder
Heart full of love,
Illuminated by light
Of the North Star above.

His slight form shaking
From his head to his toes,
Braving the cold
Of the new fallen snow.

His desire to experience
Love—in an unconditional way,
Outweighed any stocking or toy
On the miracle of Christmas Day.

FOR ROMAN AND ISAAC

Part
One

NICHOLAS

*N*icholas curled his knees to his chest, his heels pressing into the shakes of the roof to keep from sliding. Bitter wind slashed his face like a whip—a punishment, perhaps for not being tucked in bed with the other children.

He needed to see for himself. Alius and Lula told him the stories. The caroling. The feasts. Christmas Eve was rumored to be the happiest of nights, full of love and laughter. Children dressed in their finest as families celebrated a man he had yet to understand. He'd heard the tales, memorized the scriptures, but his heart longed to understand more than Father Krol's required lecture in class.

Nicholas yearned to feel Christmas.

A deep ache he couldn't ease burned to experience the true meaning, hidden behind lengthy texts and solemn prayers he hadn't quite conquered. If Nicholas could grasp it, maybe he could teach the other children at the orphanage. Maybe then, his own family would come back for him.

"Heavens, Nicholas. You'll get us all in trouble," Lula whispered from the small window above his head.

Nicholas peered over his shoulder and grinned as Lula's pale blonde-hair whipped around her angelic face. Her disapproving stare did little to threaten when backed with the warmth of her dark brown eyes. He'd marry her one day —she just didn't know it yet.

"Come out here, Lula. You can see through the window at the Swanski house."

"I don't want to see Tom Swanski, Nicholas. He throws brud in my hair and calls Alius a dwarf. Tom's awful."

With a short stature and lack of neck, Alius took the brunt of the teasing from the town. Alius couldn't help his size. Tom Swanski was a jerk, and everyone knew it. Nicholas's chest puffed out in defense of his friends. "I'll deal with Tom. Don't you worry."

Lula leaned forward. "Please, Nicholas. Please come inside."

"Look, Lula! Tom's tearing paper from that box. What is he doing?"

Lula peered from the safety of the opened window. "It's a prezent. I told you about the gifts, remember?"

Nicholas's eyes widened in wonder at the small wooden train Tom pulled from the box. The hateful, spoiled boy ran the toy along the floor in front of a large pine tree adorned with colorful paper cutouts of stars and angels. All at once, Tom ran from the room toward his mother—the train forgotten.

What Nicholas would do to receive something so wonderful. More than that, to run into the arms of someone so inviting. Caring. What had Tom done to deserve such a gift? Better yet, how awful Nicholas must have been to be deserted by his family. To be left, unloved and alone.

His eyes drifted down to his thread-bare pants an inch too short—the faded cotton shirt he'd worn for three days.

Who would want to take him home? He knew the answer. Nobody.

"Nicholas, I'm cold." Lula shivered, her arms tight around her chest as she ducked inside the shelter of the orphanage.

Nicholas snapped from his daze of self-pity and crawled up the crumbling shakes of the roof. One foot at a time, he climbed through the window frame, then looked back at the cottage on the corner celebrating Christmas.

That would be him one day. Christmas Eve night would be filled with wonder and magic. He and Lula would celebrate for days after, singing glory to the Savior. Christmas would change everything. He knew it.

A small hand slid inside his palm and pulled him toward the old wooden steps. "If Berta catches us up here, we won't be able to sit down for a week."

"She won't. It's Christmas, remember? Everyone has somewhere to be. Except us."

Nicholas and Lula tip-toed down the stairs, cringing at every creak that broke through the silence. Even though he didn't expect Berta to be on duty, someone else could be lurking in the shadows to rat them out.

They snuck into the sleep hall, a tidy room with six beds on each side, separated by old wooden tables in between. Crates underneath the wooden frame of the beds safely stored the clothes and belongings of the children. It wasn't cozy, but it was home. The only home they knew.

Lula breathed a sigh of relief when they reached their small narrow beds—side by side with twelve other children. The blanket did little against the winters in Poland, but at least it protected them from the bitter wisps of wind, seeping through the cracks in the floor and ceiling. Nicholas glanced to his right, where the soft snore of his best friend, Alius, created a cold puff of air from his mouth. On his left, his girl —Lula.

7

"Merry Christmas, Nicholas," she whispered.

He grinned. "One day, Lula. One day we'll have a Christmas like that. I promise."

NICHOLAS PUSHED HIS KASZA FROM ONE SIDE OF THE BOWL TO the other, watching the bland oats stick together in unappetizing clumps. He could feel Lula's worried gaze over his lack of appetite.

"Gonna eat that, Nic?"

Nicholas glanced across the table at his best friend and smiled. Alius stood almost two feet shorter, with an abnormally long nose and ears. The other kids enjoyed teasing him, but Nicholas knew better. Those short legs came with an even shorter fuse.

Nicholas pushed the bowl toward Alius with one finger, as if the creamy clumps had offended him. "All yours."

Alius grinned a toothy smile and wrapped his short arms around the bowl to protect it. No one was dumb enough to take it from him.

"Whatcha lookin' down about?" Alius asked around a mouthful of kasza, his bright red hair sticking up in its usual way.

Nicholas felt foolish. A mere child of twelve years old, down and out about things he didn't understand and couldn't possibly comprehend. "Just thinking, I guess."

"Come off it, Nic. Tell me."

"Do you remember your parents?" Nicholas glanced down toward the table, unable to meet the sad gaze of his friend. It was the same expression any of the children wore when asked about family. As if they mourned the loss over and over.

"I, um, I do," he muttered.

"Well? Tell me."

"We sailed for Scotland to visit Ma's family several years back. Entire boat 'bout got flooded from the storm. Right when I thought we were in the clear, my brother toppled into the water. Almost drowned." He shook his head. "I jumped in. Got him to safety, I did. Then a wave forced me under and I couldn't make it back. Sometimes . . . well, never mind."

Alius continued shoving the now dry, sticky clumps into his mouth, ignoring Nicholas's impatient stare. "What?"

"Well, sometimes I wonder if they ever noticed. You know?"

"Noticed?" Lula asked.

"That I was gone. I wonder if they even looked for me."

Nicholas's eyes widened. "Of course they did, Al. You're their son."

Alius cut his eyes toward Nicholas and smirked. "Bet ya didn't know there were two of me, did ya?"

He shook his head, confused. "Two? You mean a twin? Is that true, Alius?"

"It's true. Not as handsome, but close."

Lula grinned. "Of course not, Alius. That isn't possible."

Alius blushed at the compliment. He continued shoving spoonfuls into his mouth, fighting a bashful smile. As if something dark seeped into his thoughts, the grin vanished as quick as it came.

"He's a good brother. Kind. Smart. Everyone loves Argos. Mom and Dad used to brag about him all the time. Can't blame them, really."

Lula placed her slender hand over his and patted. "I'm certain they were just as proud of you, Alius."

He cut his eyes toward Lula. "Argos means bright and shining. Did you know that?" Alius asked.

Lula shook her head, confused.

He glanced up from his bowl. "Alius means the other one. Ironic, huh?"

Lula, bit her top lip and slipped her hand from Alius's, as if embarrassed for her friend.

"What about Christmas? Do you remember that?" Nicholas continued.

"Some of my best memories, they were. Pa got sozzled and Ma spent all day baking pies." Alius grinned at the memories. "He was crafty, my Pa. Taught me to make toys from scraps."

"Toys from scraps?" Nicholas asked, excited about the news. Why had he not heard about this before? "Can you show me?"

Alius grinned. "Sure thing, Nic."

"Nicholas?"

His spine stiffened at the high-pitched tone of Berta's voice.

"Nicholas," Lula whispered. "Berta's talking to you."

Nicholas licked his lips and swallowed, but didn't budge.

Lula nudged his elbow. "Answer her. You're going to get us all in trouble."

Nicholas cleared his throat as he slowly glanced over his shoulder, "Yes, Ms. Berta?"

"Come and have a word after breakfast. My gabinet, please." Berta continued down the aisle, unconcerned with his obvious discomfort.

He turned back in his seat, the uneven legs of the chair shifting slightly on the stone floor, as if it wavered just as much as Nicholas's courage in that moment. His eyes never left the table. In fact, he focused entirely too hard on the large split in the wood—the one that always housed a willing splinter.

"Whatcha think she wants, Nic?" Alius's eyes widened with fear.

Berta frightened everyone. Father Krol might have been in charge, but Berta was the one that kept the children in line.

Lula took a deep breath and smiled. "Who's to say it's bad? Maybe your parents have found you at last. That would be lovely!"

Nicholas smiled at her enthusiasm. He could always count on Lula to bring a bit of joy to every situation—even if only for a few minutes. "Sure, Lula. You never know, right?"

The scrape of wooden legs on the floor attracted unwanted attention from across the room as he stood. No one left during meal time—they knew better. If he was to leave the dining room, they would know why. Sad eyes watched him shuffle toward the orphan keeper, as if he'd never return.

Wooden beams hovered overhead, and the flicker of lanterns seemed to intensify as he made his way to Berta's office. The small closet of a room barely accommodated the wide wooden desk and crowded bookshelf, not to mention, Berta herself. A tall gray-haired woman with a thick Polish accent, Berta was just as round as she was tall. Beady narrow eyes watched every move inside the orphanage through thick glasses. And worst of all—three coarse black hairs jutting from her barely-there chin.

Terrifying.

These were the things people remembered, weren't they? The shallow, unimportant details that told nothing of a person's true character. Even at Nicholas's young age, he had learned to appreciate the actions of those around him. The way Berta sat beside the bed of a sick child throughout the night. The worry in her gaze for the orphans who left her care. The tears she tried to hide, as her sniffles echoed down the halls.

Berta was strict, but kind. Yes, she'd threatened to whip

them with a switch until they couldn't sit, but Nicholas had never known her to follow through. He stepped into the doorway of Berta's gabinet, waiting for her to acknowledge him. Nicholas inhaled the mustiness of old books and dried tea leaves, the familiar smell of herbata comforting him.

"Are you going to stand there all day? Come. Sit." Berta continued scribbling, not bothering to glance up.

Nicholas stepped forward and sat in the small chair across from Berta. He waited silently until she placed her pencil on the desk and clasped her pale hands together. She lowered her head to peer at him over her glasses.

"Now. Nicholas. I'd like to ask you about a complaint I received."

"A complaint, Ma'am?"

She tilted her head to the side. "A neighbor noticed a young boy on the roof of the orphanage peeking through her windows. Naturally, the lady was quite distraught. Her husband came straight away this morning to file an official complaint."

Nicholas lowered his head, ashamed. He should've known he'd get caught.

She cleared her throat. "Ah, I see. Were you alone?"

"Yes, Ma'am."

"So a sweet little blonde didn't follow along behind you?" One brow raised at her question. "Like she always does . . ."

Nicholas frantically shook his head. "No, Ma'am."

Berta chuckled. "I didn't expect you to give her away. You're far too noble for that Nicholas Dalbeck. Tell me, whatever were you doing?"

"Doing?"

"On the roof."

Nicholas swallowed. "Just curious, Ms. Berta."

Berta narrowed her eyes further, if that was possible. "Curious about what, Child?"

"Christmas, Ma'am. It fascinates me. What it feels like . . . where it started."

"Why, Nicholas. Father Krol always gives a lovely interpretation of where Christmas comes from. If I recall, I do believe the widow up the street sent honey cakes for all of the children this year."

"Yes, Ma'am. I'm grateful, please don't think I'm not. There's just something inside me that says there's more—something only a child with a family understands."

Berta sat back in her chair, as if startled by his words. "I see." She looked over his head, staring at nothing in particular as she spoke carefully. "Nicholas, Christmas is a holy celebration for families, not something to be disrespected or interrupted. Do you understand what I'm saying?" Her gaze traveled back to his face, and her eyes held sympathy even a child could see. "You're forbidden from going to the roof again. Next time, Lula Dunivant will be punished alongside you."

Nicholas's light blue eyes glistened with unshed tears. He nodded only once, for fear of shaking them free. "Yes, Ma'am. Can I be excused now?"

She sighed. "Yes, of course."

Nicholas stood to leave, but stopped at the doorway. For the first time in his life, he asked the question that he'd never had the courage to voice until that day.

"Where did I come from?"

Berta crossed her arms in front of her chest. "What's going on, Nicholas? What brought this about?"

"I'm curious, Ms. Berta. I've never asked about my past. I need to know who I am so I don't feel so lost."

She nodded at his words. "Alright. You were an infant, abandoned at a church in Dalbeca—St. Mary's, I believe. You were given the surname Dalbeck for that reason. There isn't much to tell you, Nicholas. I'm sorry."

He deflated. Not even a last name that meant anything. "What about the name Nicholas? Where did that come from?" he asked, hopeful.

She smiled, sadly. "The priest. I'm uncertain why, but that is how he introduced you to us."

He nodded. "Thank you, Ms. Berta. I need to get to my studies."

"You're a good boy, Nicholas. One day, you will find what you're looking for. I promise."

"DALBECK. WHAT KIND OF NAME IS DALBECK, ANYWAY? MIGHT as well call me Nicholas Roundbottom, or Nicholas Fatlip," he mumbled to himself. Berta's words did little to fill the emptiness he felt inside. A single drop of water in a dry well.

"Shh, Nic. You know you can't talk during class," Alius scolded. "Father Krol is watching you."

Nicholas huffed and rolled his eyes at his annoyed friend. He stared at the script about temperatures, reading the same passage over and over, taking nothing in. He shifted from hip to hip, the uneven desk creaking loudly with every move he made. The seat was so old, he figured Daniel Fahrenheit himself had sat there as a child. He wouldn't doubt it.

Nicholas's forehead hit the desk in frustration, and Alius gasped at his boldness. He wanted to know more about Christmas, his family, and the priest who named him. He yearned to know things that didn't involve the measurement of temperature.

His mood didn't improve throughout the day, as he pushed a spoonful of gulasz from one side of his bowl to the other at dinner, unable to eat. Alius and Lula left the table to finish their chores before bed, while he stayed to sweep the dining hall.

Frayed ends of the straw broom swept against stone floors, the curled edges refusing to touch the smallest of grooves—back and forth, until Nicholas realized he'd been in the same spot for several minutes.

He knew he would never be satisfied until he learned more. Berta had told him just enough to rouse his curiosity and he couldn't control the deep-seated need to immerse himself in his history, so he had a chance of experiencing something more.

Something *grand*.

Most of the children had drifted off hours before, deep into dreams of what tomorrow would hold. Nicholas knew better. He'd been at the orphanage his entire life and had seen very few children adopted. His gaze traveled around the room, taking in every child sleeping on the old rickety beds, a child who'd never know Christmas. Just like him.

His thoughts drifted to Berta. What had life been like for her, before her husband's passing? Before she stepped into the role no one else would consider. Who would move to a poor, poverty-ridden town to look after abandoned children? Only the kindest of souls. The most selfless, like Berta.

"Go to sleep, Nicholas." Lula propped up on one elbow, narrowing her dark eyes at him. "Honestly, I can hear your thoughts from over here."

Nicholas grinned. "Really? Then I guess you know how pretty I thought you looked today."

Even in the dark, the flush of her cheeks were visible.

"Um . . . Ew! I don't need to be hearin' that," Alius grumbled.

Nicholas cleared his throat, abruptly changing the subject. "I'm calling a meeting," he declared.

"Now?" Alius and Lula questioned together.

"Yes," he insisted. Nicholas rolled from his bed, ungracefully, but considered it smooth and swift as his legs hit the cold wooden planks.

Lula and Alius followed his lead to the floor, where they crawled to where he'd ducked beside his bed.

"What is this about, Nicholas? If Berta . . ." Lula whispered.

"I want to know what Christmas feels like."

Lula frowned. "I don't understand."

Nicholas sighed. "Something about Christmas calls to me —fascinates me. On Christmas Eve night, I feel alive." He glanced up at his faithful companions. "I want to find Christmas spirit for the orphanage. Everyone deserves to celebrate it, even us."

"But, we do celebrate Christmas," Lula whispered.

"No, we learn about the history behind it. We go through motions we don't understand, Lula. We need to experience it. If what they say is true, and our Savior was born on that night, there must be more."

Alius cleared his throat, as if preparing to be honest with his friend. "I get it, Nic. I miss Christmas, too. But I don't see how we can do this. We're just kids."

"He's right, Nicholas. The celebration is for children with moms and dads. It isn't meant for us." Lula's dark brown eyes filled with sadness at the truth of her words. "I'm sorry."

Nicholas stared at the sorrowful eyes of his friends, longing for something outside the four walls of the orphanage—just as he did.

"It doesn't have to be that way. We can change it."

Lula reached for Nicholas's hand and whispered, "How are we supposed to do that?"

"We have to run away."

LULA

"Nicholas, where would we go? How would we survive?" She watched his eyes light up like the North Star at the thought of leaving. Did he understand what he asked of them? To give up their security, their shelter? They were only children.

Nicholas ran his hand through his brown shaggy hair that curled around his ears. It needed a trim. The tiny strip of moonlight shining through the window pane highlighted the blue of his eyes—a twinkle at just the mention of Christmas.

"Berta said Christmas is a special time for family. I have to find my parents. If I can experience the spirit of Christmas, I can share it with everyone. I'll make sure no one is left out." Nicholas looked down at the floor and shook his head. "It isn't right."

"It won't be easy, Nic. Someone could catch us—send us back to the orphanage or somewhere worse." After a few seconds, Alius shrugged. "Even so, I'm with you, Lad. I'd love nothing more than to find my family."

Both boys glanced at Lula, waiting patiently.

She swallowed, unable to think straight with them

focused so intently on her decision. Did she want to go? Of course. Was she scared? Terrified.

Nicholas placed his hand over hers and squeezed. "Think about it, okay?"

She shook her head. "It's not that I don't want to go with you. I've been nowhere other than the orphanage in years. I won't be much help."

"Alius has, Lula. He can guide us. Right, Al?"

"Sure. It's been a few years, but I still know my way around."

Nicholas squeezed her hand, comforting her. "You don't have to go, Lula. I promise I'll come back for you."

"You will?" she asked.

"Of course. I'm gonna marry you."

Lula blushed at the blue-eyed boy with rosy cheeks smirking in her direction.

She was counting on it.

RECESS WASN'T LULA'S FAVORITE TIME OF THE DAY, considering the weather. With her knees tucked under her skirt on the cold snow-covered ground, she shivered and rubbed her hands together, frozen from the brutal winter. Alius, with a collection of tin cans, twigs and string, attempted to teach Nicholas the art of toy-making.

"Are you sure, Alius? This doesn't look like a horse." Nicholas didn't appear impressed.

"Well, you have to use a bit of imagination, now Nicholas." Alius turned the can sideways to demonstrate. "See there? A silver stallion—a courageous beast of tin, faster than any train ever built."

Lula fought a smile. "It's lovely, Alius. Really."

He held the small tin can out for Lula, decorated with twigs and trash. "For you m'lady."

Lula gently picked up the prized possession and held it as if it were glass. "Oh my. I'm speechless."

Alius stood, dusting the snow from his short legs. "My work here is done." He walked toward the back door of the orphanage without another word.

Nicholas tightened his lips, trying not to laugh.

Lula lifted the clump of trash, rotating and inspecting it. "I've never had a prezent before, you know. Trash or not, I shall cherish it forever."

Nicholas peaked around Lula, as if verifying Alius was indeed gone. "You know, I made something for you, too." His cheeks flushed pink as he peeked up toward her.

She waited, whether he was too shy or enjoyed torturing her—she wasn't sure. After a solid thirty seconds of patience, she snapped.

"Are you teasing me, Nicholas Dalbeck? It's not nice if you are."

Nicholas held out his dirt-covered fist, clenched tight around the hidden treasure. He wouldn't meet Lula's gaze. "It isn't much," he whispered.

When he opened his hand, a small wire, formed in a circle and twisted in a cluster at the top, sat in the center of his palm. "I'm going to buy you a proper ring one day, I promise." Nicholas pushed his gift toward Lula's face until she grasped the small ring between her fingers.

"I don't need another one. This is perfect." Lula slid the small circle of silver wire on her finger, shaping it against her skin so it wouldn't slide off.

"We'll always be together. All three of us."

Lula grinned. "Forever."

AS EXPECTED, NICHOLAS CALLED A MEETING THAT NIGHT after everyone else had drifted off to sleep. Lula and Alius rolled from their small beds, the creak of wood exaggerated by the dead silence in the room.

Lula held back her giggle at the grave, downcast expression on Nicholas's face—the clenched jaw, wide eyes and stiff posture. She hid her amusement well. This journey was important to him, and she would support him in any way possible. After all, he was her forever. Lula twisted the ring back and forth on her petite finger as she absorbed his plan, memorizing every detail.

"Our only hope is the train," Nicholas whispered. "I think we should leave on New Year's Day."

Lula gasped. "That soon?"

Nicholas shrugged. "I don't see why not."

"The train? Are you mad, Nic?" Alius lowered his voice. "That's quite a haul."

Nicholas shook his head. "We can't take a horse. They'd for sure find us, Alius. A train is perfect. We can hide until it's safe to jump off. Dalbeca isn't far."

"Dalbeca? How far? Why are we going there?" Alius asked.

"You don't know? You said you could guide us, Alius," Nicholas replied.

Alius had the decency to look embarrassed.

Nicholas shook his head and continued. "That's where my parents abandoned me. At a church. Someone could remember something, anything that might help me locate them."

Lula's chest tightened, her sympathetic heart aching for what he might find. "If they can't help? What then?"

Nicholas stared off in space. "We find Alius's family. Eventually we'll find someone to help us. We have to. What about you, Lula? Do you know anything about your parents?"

"Mother passed when I was small. Sometimes she acted afraid, as if someone was after us. It was strange. I remember the ginger of her hair and her fading brown eyes. Then, one morning she never woke." There weren't many memories of her mother, but the ones she had were pleasant. . . loving.

"Gee, Lu. Sorry 'bout that." Alius mumbled. "What about your Pa?"

Lula had been thankful they'd never asked before that day. She didn't want her friends to look down on her—pity her. She swallowed before answering. "I have no memories of him. Not sure he was ever around."

Nicholas and Alius looked away at hearing Lula's scandalous confession about her mother. She hoped they didn't think less of her.

Nicholas cleared his throat. "If that's the sort of man he was, you didn't need him anyway, Lula. You have us."

Alius nodded, but still refused to meet her gaze.

Nicholas continued. "My family abandoned me. Doesn't sound like they were much better. Maybe we would be better off searching for Alius's parents."

"Nic," Alius started. "We need to go to Dalbeca. If we don't, you'll always wonder if you would've found them. If you would've found your Christmas spirit."

Lula knew Alius was right. This wasn't the first year Nicholas fought with the desire to experience the mysterious holiday of feast, family and gifts. Something deep inside of him yearned for it. She had watched, year after year, as the shaggy-haired boy with blue eyes dreamt of celebrating the way others do on Christmas Eve night. Nicholas needed to find himself.

"You know he's right," Lula whispered.

Nicholas's intense gaze burned through Lula, and she knew the question that he'd wanted to ask all day..

"Are you coming with us?" he asked.

Lula breathed through the fear and sadness of abandoning her shelter—her security. Could she do it? She longed to leave with them more than anything, but her lack of courage mocked her. She wasn't as brave . . . or strong.

Lula shook her head. "I'm sorry."

Nicholas forced a smile and gripped her hand. His thumb grazed across her wire ring, bent and discolored. His promise to her.

"I'll be back for you."

"I know you will."

"HOW MUCH YOU SWIPE, NIC?" ALIUS SQUATTED BESIDE THE bed, unfolding a cloth of stale rye bread and dried fruit he'd saved from his plate the past week.

Nicholas sighed. "Won't get us far. You?"

"Five slices of bread. No fruit." Alius glanced down, as if ashamed. "Sorry, Nic. Got hungry."

Lula had watched the boys the past few days, collecting every scrap of food they could find to take on their journey. Hiding slices of bread or apples in the pocket of their trousers until they could sneak out of the dining hall. She glanced down at the sad excuse of a bounty. It wasn't enough.

"It's alright. We'll try again tonight. We only have a couple more days to get what we need. Lula, were you able to grab a couple of blankets from the laundry?"

She nodded. "There are four folded under my bed. I also found a couple of potato sacks to hold your things."

"Smart thinking. What would we do without you?"

Nicholas's smile held a smidge of sadness, clear in the tightness of his lips.

"I believe the question is what will I do without the two of you?"

Silence enveloped the small circle of friends, as Lula kneeled on the rough wood floor—the sadness of separation entwined with anticipation of an exciting journey before them. A thrilling discovery of their past along with fear of their future.

There were no words to describe the emotion that welled inside Lula. Could she let them leave, not knowing what lay ahead? She climbed into her bed that night, staring at the rotted planks on the ceiling as sleep refused to claim her. This life had aged them—matured them. How could there be so much they didn't know, but felt as though they'd lived a lifetime?

Tossing and turning, she spun to her right, to find Nicholas's observant gaze transfixed on her face.

"Nicholas? What's the matter?"

"I'm just memorizing."

Lula's brow furrowed at his words. "Memorizing?"

"You. Your hair, dark eyes and the way you chew your lip when there's something on your mind." He grinned a boyishly cute half-smile. "I don't want to forget."

Lula sighed, unable to respond. She laid on her side, staring at Nicholas until the heaviness of sleep was too strong to ignore. When Lula finally closed her eyes, she dreamt of a life filled with love, family and Christmas.

NICHOLAS KICKED A PEBBLE DOWN THE HALL, MUMBLING about his lack of success at dinner. One slice of bread with the stew—that's all they'd served. Lula knew he and Alius had planned to pack a week's worth of rations, but they had a few days at best.

As they walked into the sleeping hall, ten to twelve children stood quietly, watching them enter with suspiciousness in their gaze. Nicholas faltered, as if the unusual crowd of kids stunned him. Not Lula. She knew why they were there.

William, the oldest at fifteen, stepped forward. He was known for keeping to himself and his quiet nature, along with his size, intimidated the other children. William crossed his arms over his chest and peered at Nicholas. "Hear ya gonna run away. That true?"

Nicholas cleared his throat, then stood straight and tall. "It's true. I plan to bring back Christmas."

"Christmas?" William asked, tilting his head to the side.

"That's right." Nicholas lifted his chin higher. "Christmas should be for everyone. I intend to make that happen."

William stepped forward, almost a foot taller than Nicholas. Everyone in the room held their breath, waiting for an altercation. William grinned and shook his head. When he uncrossed his arms, William held two fist-fulls of bread. He sat the food on the end of Nicholas's bed, then reached to shake his hand.

"Safe travels, Dalbeck." William turned and left the room.

One by one, each child followed William's lead, placing a handful of bread, wafers or fruit on the bed for the voyage. Nicholas and Alius watched wide-eyed at the mountain of food piling up. When all of the children had left the room, Nicholas slowly spun toward Lula.

"It was you, wasn't it? You did this."

Lula shuffled from foot to foot, unable to look them in the eye. "I know it was risky, one of them could rat you out at any moment. But I couldn't let you starve."

Neither of the boys responded, but stepped forward and wrapped Lula in their arms. This beautiful and everlasting family they'd built, inside the timeworn walls of an orphanage in Poland, would mean more to Lula than anything they could ever discover. More than parents, holidays or gifts under a fresh-cut pine.

It always would.

SOFT, WARM LIPS BRUSHED ACROSS LULA'S FOREHEAD AS SHE feigned sleep. She'd fought to keep her lids shut as the clothes and bags rustled in the bed next to hers. They were leaving. If she woke to say goodbye, Nicholas would see the tears—the pain she felt by just the thought of his absence. No, she wouldn't make it difficult.

Lula couldn't be sure when it happened. Maybe the moment his warm skin left hers—the creak of the uneven door as they closed it one final time—or even the moment she glanced toward her right, staring at the empty bed through a blur of tears.

She couldn't stay without them.

Nicholas and Alius were her shelter, not the orphanage. Lula jumped from the bed, pulling on every scrap of clothing she owned—layering socks, pants and shirts to shield her from the unyielding winter wind. She slipped into her worn boots and ripped the blanket from the bed, tying it around her neck. Glancing over her shoulder at the small room once more, she left the safety of the orphanage to find Nicholas and Alius.

Lula slipped out the back door by the old tin wash tub and stayed close to the building, out of sight. The fresh layer of white powder provided a clear path of the boy's boots into the treeline behind the orphanage. Traveling in the woods was smart. It would take longer to reach the train tracks, but it would keep them out of sight—hidden from curious eyes that might halt their journey.

Carefully, she stepped into the forest, following their trail. Her small feet vanished as they sunk into the thick snow, icy flakes fighting their way into the tops of her boots. Thick roots and branches stretched across the ground, weighed down by layers of snow as a small sliver of moonlight peeked through the top of the trees.

Lula knew she wasn't as quick as they were and she'd have to fight to catch up. Her short legs fumbled through the thick of the brush and her heart pounded at the whistle of a train up ahead. She ran, losing her balance and toppling in the snow more times than she could count. Brisk air chilled the beads of sweat running down her brow.

She broke through the tree-line, her lungs burning from the exertion. She could barely make out two slight forms in the dark, jumping on an open train car. Lula bolted forward, the thin blanket around her neck blowing in the chilly wind like a cape. She pushed forward through the snow—determined to reach them.

As the loud whistle rang out across the night sky, Lula realized she couldn't hold out any longer. Blue eyes filled with panic met hers from the sliding door of the train as Nicholas reached his hand out for hers. Exhaustion won out as Lula's legs gave way and her body tumbled forward.

3

NICHOLAS

*N*icholas gripped the sleeve of Lula's coat as she collapsed toward the ground. As he jumped forward to grab her, Alius kept a firm hold on him from behind. Her thin legs dragged along the ice-covered rock as they fought to pull her aboard the moving train. One fierce tug, and Lula pushed off the heel of her boot, propelling her into the car on top of Nicholas.

He laid perfectly still—the impact forcing the breath from his lungs.

After a few seconds, he raised his head to meet large brown eyes peering down at him. "I didn't tell you goodbye."

Lula burst out giggling, collapsing against Nicholas's chest as he fought to catch his breath around the contagious laughter. Alius stood over them with his arms crossed and his brow furrowed, shaking his head.

"You've all gone looney, you have. Could've been killed," Alius barked.

Nicholas and Lula's delirium continued—escalated by the look of disgust on their short friend's face. Alius waved his arms in frustration as he spun, taking his place in the dark corner of the train.

The echo of laughter ceased as Nicholas stared up at Lula. "You came."

She sighed. "There is nothing back there for me. Not without you and Alius."

He smiled. "Especially me, right?"

Lula pushed off his chest and rolled her eyes, leaving the question unanswered.

"You?" Alius asked. "Who's gonna make Lula laugh if I'm not around? Definitely not the love in your weepy eyes. Gross."

A soft snore in the opposite corner of the train quickly interrupted their light-hearted chuckles. Large crates and boxes occupied most of the old wooden planks of the floor, so they crept around the side as if someone would jump out at any moment. Nicholas stood in front of his friends, stretching his neck to investigate the sound.

Silence.

"Who's there?" Nicholas called out.

He stepped forward, peeking around the large crate in front of him. His gaze traveled along the floor, searching for a threat, but the darkness of the night didn't make it easy. Suddenly, through a break in the mountains, the moonlight illuminated a huddled figure on the floor. Nicholas leaned closer, hoping to get a better look at the mysterious passenger.

The worn board underneath Nicholas's boot creaked through the silence, startling the sleeping stranger. A man bolted upright, eyes wide as saucers as he slid into a tight ball in the corner. His salt and pepper hair, greasy and over-grown, stuck up in all directions as black smut from the train highlighted his blue eyes. A thin brown jacket was the only thing to shield him from the winter storm.

Nicholas held both palms in the air. "We mean no harm."

The pitiful soul exhaled out of relief, then wiped his nose on the sleeve of the dirty jacket. "Frightened me. Waking a man while he sleeps . . ."

"My apologies," Nicholas replied. "What's your name?"

"Name's Tomek. You?"

"Nicholas. That's Lula and Alius." He pointed behind him.

Tomek peered around Nicholas, his left eye opening wider than his right, to get a better look at his companions. "You're just kids—all of ya."

All three cut their eyes at each other, as if they feared he'd send them back to the orphanage. Alius cleared his throat, speaking for the first time. "Where ya headed?"

"Headed?" A cackle erupted in Tomek's throat that soon turned into a belly laugh. "Oh yeah. I got some place to be alright. Somewhere important."

Alius stepped forward and whispered. "You think he's mad?"

Lula shrugged her shoulders.

Something about the frailty of the man brought forth a deep-seated need to help. Nicholas had little, but he'd learned at a very young age that kindness had a way of returning when you least expected it. Pulling one of the small brown blankets from the potato sack, he glanced up to Lula's sweet smile and Alius's mouth hanging open in shock.

He exhaled, then turned to where Tomek sat shaking. "Here." Nicholas held it out, waiting for him to accept.

Tomek inspected the small square of fabric. "You'll be needing that. Keep it."

"We have an extra. We'd like for you to have it." He nodded.

Tomek narrowed his eyes at Nicholas. "You afraid I'll turn you in, Boy? Is that why you're being so generous?"

Nicholas shook his head.

"Then why?"

"You need it." Nicholas shrugged. "Plus, one day when I'm in need, I hope kindness will find its way back to me."

Tomek grunted, as if he contemplated Nicholas's words. He reached for the blanket slowly, still debating if there was an ulterior motive. Tomek clutched it to his chest, and his eyes filled with tears. He nodded. "Thank you. Like Christmas morning, it is."

Nicholas's eyes widened, and he stepped forward. "Tell me. Tell me about Christmas."

The stranger's brow furrowed in confusion, then sadness filled his eyes. "I need to get some rest. Better huddle up—it's gonna be a cold one."

Fresh snowflakes, carried by the brisk wind, kissed the tip of Nicholas's nose, creating chills across his skin. He blinked, the train blurry and dreamlike from sleep. Nicholas sat up and stretched. The hard surface caused a deep ache across his back and the stiffness begged to be relieved.

Although cold, the quiet night sky calmed the anxiety of the coming days. What would they find? How would they live? His gaze traveled to the sliding door where Tomek sat, his legs dangling over the side of the train. Glancing down at Alius and Lula fast asleep, he silently crept past them, making his way to the mysterious stranger.

Tomek intrigued Nicholas.

Nicholas shuffled up beside him, sitting down in the same fashion. Although he never looked his way, Tomek must have known he was there. Nicholas wasn't a small kid—he was hard to miss.

The glint of bright stars appeared larger that night, closer than ever before, as they created a magical backdrop over the mountains of snow in the distance. Nicholas took a deep breath and tilted his head toward the night sky.

"Sorry if the open door woke you. I needed fresh air." Tomek took a deep breath. "It's a sight, isn't it? Never gets old."

Nicholas nodded but didn't answer.

"How old are you?" Tomek asked.

"Twelve."

He grunted. "You're big for twelve. What's a young kid doin' out here?"

Nicholas reached into his pocket, pulling two stale wafers free. He handed one to Tomek before answering. "I want to find my family."

"You lost?"

He shook his head. "Orphaned."

Tomek bit into the stale crisp. "Blimey, Son. Why would you want to find 'em? Probably no good for nothin' anyway."

"That's the only way for me to find my Christmas spirit. I have to experience it with them so I can share it with the other children at the orphanage."

Tomek's gaze drifted back to the night sky, the hard crunch of the wafer the only sound. He sighed before whispering, "You asked me to tell you about Christmas. That right?"

Nicholas sat up straight. "Yes, Sir." He held his breath as he waited for words he'd longed to hear. Everything—he wanted to know it all.

"I'm afraid my memories are slight at best. I can tell you what I remember as a young lad."

Nicholas nodded again—his eyes wide with wonder and intrigue.

"Christmas Eve, before the sun rose across the sky or the roosters crowed, I'd wake filled with the magic of the unknown. Might be a pair of shoes—could be a toy carved by

Grandpops. The unexpected gift waiting for me was thrilling, I tell you. More than that, the feast Ma spent all day preparing for us. Fresh karp, red beet soup, cabbage . . .we'd eat off that meal for a week. I'd seen nothing like it."

"Sounds wonderful, Tomek."

"Ma was brilliant in the kitchen—every bite of poppy seed cake or kobler filled with the love of family. Well, in my case anyway. Not so much in yours." He elbowed Nicholas, teasing him.

"The magic never faded, even as I aged. Miriam and I used to sit around talking about the traditions we would create with our family." He looked away from Nicholas and cleared his throat. "But that never happened."

"What happened to them?" Nicholas asked.

"Sometimes people make bad choices. Decisions they look back on and regret the rest of their lives. It causes pain, heartache, and most of all distance between you and those you love."

Nicholas absorbed Tomek's words, determined to make good choices and keep his friends close. "Is that what happened? You did something bad?"

Tomek frowned. "I did. Tried to take it back, you know. But I was too late."

"How long has it been since you've seen your family?" Nicholas asked. Tomek was the adult version of an orphan, longing for the love of a family he'd lost along the way.

"My wife and child died long ago. My parents—it's been years, I'm afraid. Who knows if they're still alive. They wouldn't have me if they were."

His chin quivered from the memory, and Nicholas refrained from reaching out to comfort him. He sat beside Tomek, in comfortable silence, hoping companionship was enough. Nicholas wasn't sure how much time had gone by—it could have been thirty minutes or two hours.

He sat on the side of the train with Tomek, absorbing the fresh winter air and ignoring the icy numbness in his fingertips.

"Where are you going, anyway?" Tomek asked.

"Dalbeca."

"No train stops in Dalbeca, I'm afraid. You'll have to jump and walk the rest of the way. By my estimate, shortly after sunrise tomorrow."

"Not sure who will love that more, Lula or Alius," Nicholas said, sarcastically.

"WE HAVE TO DO WHAT?" ALIUS ASKED.

If he'd had money to gamble, Nicholas would have bet on Lula being upset about jumping from a moving train in an unknown land.

He would have lost.

Alius was visibly shaking from head to toe. Lula's eyes were bright and excited as she bounced around the train, anticipating the moment they would leap dangerously from the locomotive.

Her lack of fear concerned him.

"Relax, Alius," Lula soothed. "We aren't moving that fast." She placed her hand on his arm to reassure him.

He didn't look comforted. "Don't give me those big brown eyes, Lula. It doesn't work on me."

Lula swung her head toward Nicholas, annoyed. "We will have to push him."

"Push me?" Alius exclaimed. "Are you mad?"

Throaty chuckles pulled their attention toward the corner where Tomek's eyes lit up, amused. "Full of courage, this one."

Nicholas wasn't sure if it was a sarcastic comment about

Alius, or an observation of Lula. Either way, he ignored it. "Alius, it will be fine. Jump and roll. Got it?"

"Do I have a choice?"

"You can stay with me." Tomek grinned more toothy than usual.

Alius turned toward Nicholas with narrowed eyes. "I dislike you very much right now."

Tomek stood, leaning against the sliding door of the car. "I'd prepare if I were you. Looks to be less than a kilometer away."

Lula stood on her toes, attempting to glance down the track. "Where are we jumping, anyway?"

"If it were me, I'd jump right after the tunnel. The deep ditches should be full of fresh snow and make for a softer landing. You'll walk for a bit until you reach the dirt road by the creek. Follow that path to Dalbeca."

"Thank you, Tomek. Who knows where we would have ended up without you."

Alius sighed. "Not jumping from a train, maybe?" He crossed his arms over his chest and glared.

Nicholas tied the potato sacks, preparing to throw them out ahead of their jump. "Come now, Alius. It might be fun."

Alius's head turned slowly toward his friend, as if awkwardly attached. "Fun? Is this what you normally do for fun, Nic?"

"Get ready kids. It's coming up," Tomek called out.

Nicholas shook Tomek's hand and smiled. "Good to have met you, Tomek."

A hint of a smile graced Tomek's face. "There's something 'bout you, kid. Something special." Tomek shook his head. "If you find trouble, you know where I'm at. Maybe we'll meet again one day."

Nicholas nodded and stepped toward the open door. Lula

stood beside him, giddy, as Alius plastered himself against the corner of the car.

"Come now, Alius. It's almost time," Lula coaxed.

"I'll catch up. Promise." Alius mumbled, somewhat out of breath from anxiety.

The dark tunnel swallowed the length of the train and Nicholas anticipated their leap. He leaned in close, whispering to Lula, "We have to get him moving, it's almost time. Can you use your soothing voice or something?"

Lula nodded. "Alius, dear. Come, stand beside me and take a look. It's not bad, I promise. If you're still unsure, we'll wait for a safer drop-off."

Alius's face popped up from his position in the corner. He appeared to have his head between his knees. "Really?"

"Of course. We aren't trying to pressure you."

Alius shuffled toward the opening as the train exited the murkiness of the stone tunnel. He glanced over the edge at the snow covered drop and without warning, Lula shoved Alius from the train. Short arms and legs flailed mid-air, as a combination of a cry and a very feminine shriek reverberated against the mountainside.

Nicholas jerked his head toward Lula, in shock. Had she actually pushed Alius from the train?

She shrugged. "He wouldn't jump." Lula took a couple of steps back and ran forward to make her exit. Nicholas watched as she gracefully sailed through the air and rolled safely down the snowbank. He threw the supplies out and glanced once more over his shoulder toward Tomek, who watched him with interest. "I hope you find what you're looking for."

"Me too." Nicholas replied.

He leaped from the side, positioning his body to roll down the ditch. It wasn't as easy as Lula made it look. Although the powder broke his fall, the impact jarred him and he bit the side of his tongue. Snow, cold and wet, coated his cheeks as he rolled, and crept into the neck of his coat.

After tumbling maybe ten feet, he landed on his back, breathing heavy from adrenaline with the taste of copper on his tongue. Big brown eyes peered down at him, full of excitement.

"We must do that again!" Lula exclaimed.

Nicholas pushed up on his elbows and glared. "Are you insane?"

He scrambled to his feet, pausing to make sure the dizziness had run its course. Tall pines and birch trees towered over them, but very little brush could be seen peeking up from the white blanket of snowfall. He struggled to get his bearings from where he stood, but Tomek had told him to walk straight ahead from the tracks to find the creek. That shouldn't be difficult.

"Where's Alius?" He stretched his neck from side to side, searching for his friend.

Lula didn't respond, but pointed toward a large Pine tree in the distance. Underneath laid Alius, unmoving.

"Is he alright?" Nicholas asked, panicked.

Lula rolled her eyes. "He's fine. He's giving me the silent treatment."

Nicholas grinned, blocking the sun with his hand. "I can't imagine why."

"What was I supposed to do? Leave him on the train?"

Nicholas trudged through the dense snow toward Alius. "Remind me never to cross you."

"You'll do well to remember that, Nicholas Dalbeck."

He chuckled under his breath, then glanced down at the sight of his short, stumpy friend wedged in the depth of the winter snow. Alius didn't look toward either of them, but he knew they were there.

"Are you hurt, Alius?"

"Only my pride," he mumbled.

Nicholas shuffled behind him, cupping under his arms to help him stand, then made his way over toward the supplies.

Alius slowly turned toward Lula and pursed his lips. "Evil, you are."

Lula smirked. "It worked, didn't it?"

4

NICHOLAS

*S*unlight shining overhead fought to pierce the tree-covered forest they'd found themselves in. Tomek told them they would have to walk for a bit, but this seemed excessive. More than rest—they needed water.

"Not sure why you're trusting the crazy man from the train, Nic. He didn't come across as the wisest. Just sayin'," Alius mumbled.

"I don't see anyone else offering to help, Alius. Might as well give it a go."

"Why do you think he was on the train, anyway? Doesn't he have a home? A family? Do you think he's a thief? A murderer? What if we barely escaped with our lives?" Alius gasped.

Nicholas knew the answer to those questions, but didn't share. He might not have known the details, but he'd heard enough. It wasn't his story to tell. He felt sorry for Tomek.

"If that's the case, I guess I saved your life back there, Alius." Lula fought an over-confident smile.

He mumbled, "He could lead us into a trap, you know.

We'd be snatched up and sent back by tomorrow if we trust every loony we come in contact with."

Nicholas shook his head. No point in arguing. Plus, he wanted nothing more than to take in every sight and smell surrounding him. The wildlife in the area seemed somewhat scarce—very few rabbits or squirrels were seen running about. The heavy scent of evergreen enveloped him . . . comforted him.

All at once, the snap of a twig sounded in the distance and the deep chuckle of a grown man reflected off the trees. Nicholas held his hand up to halt Alius and Lula. His gaze traveled over every inch of the snow covered forest, searching for the unknown visitor he knew was close by. His shaky breath and pounding heart drowned out every other noise. So much for comfort. He turned slowly, making eye contact with Alius.

"Do you see the overturned log to your right? Get behind it and stay there. Don't make a peep," he whispered.

Alius nodded.

"Lula, get behind the tree on your left. You're small enough to stay out of sight if you press yourself against it. Alright?"

Lula eased toward the rough bark of the pine, keeping a close eye out for a threat.

Nicholas squatted down, scanning the woods for danger. He placed one boot in front of the other, taking small, silent steps through the snow. Again, a throaty voice rang out.

"'Tis only the middle of winter, Lech! Nie worry yourself 'bout catching the fever! Swashbuckler!" A gravelly female voice shouted out.

It reminded Nicholas of someone who'd smoked a pipe for years.

Again, deep throaty chuckles rang out. "Aye, my love. The

water is icy, but fine. You could accompany your dear husband."

"Nie in this lifetime!" she shouted. "I plan on livin' long after you leave this world!"

"Ula. . . don't be like that. Just a quick dip and I'll be out. You don't want me smellin' like the pigs."

"Sleepin' with the pigs is what you'll be doin'. Get yer clothes on!"

Nicholas could hear it—the rush of fresh water over rocks ahead. They were close to the river. He stepped forward once again, stretching his neck to get a better view. The loud crunch of a pine cone under his boot halted the noise up ahead.

"What was that, Lech? I think someone's here. Get your dupa outta the creek and get a move on."

"Calm yourself, woman. I'm comin' out."

Nicholas peeked around the large tree he'd hidden behind just in time to see the largest, hairiest rear imaginable standing on the creek bank. He wrinkled his nose in shock.

"Gettin' your eyes full, eh Ula?"

Ula growled and stomped off in the opposite direction as Lech slid into his trousers and followed her—laughing along the way.

Nicholas waited several minutes before signaling Alius and Lula to come out.

"What was that all about?" Alius asked.

"Well." Nicholas swallowed. "You missed a hairy dupa. Other than that, I believe we're safe."

Lula threw her hand over her mouth in shock. "I can live the rest of my life without seeing that!"

Alius chuckled at her obvious disgust. "Let's get a move on. I could use a quencher, Nic."

"What ye doin' out here alone?" A deep voice rumbled.

The children spun at the sound of the strange man's

voice. Nicholas recognized him from the creek. He'd never forget that sight.

"Just taking a walk, Sir. Didn't mean to interrupt your —bath."

Lech chuckled. "Saw that, did ye? Makes me wife angry, says I'll get the fever. That's the only reason I do it."

Nicholas stared, unable to respond. Why in the world would you want to make your wife angry? "We're just passing through, so we'll be out of your way."

Nicholas stepped to the left, and Lech matched his step, blocking him. "What's in ye bag?"

"Bag?" Nicholas asked. He turned his head, looking at the potato sack over his shoulder. "These? Nothing much. Old blankets, some clothes . . ."

"Food?" Lech asked.

Ula smirked as she walked up beside her husband. "Told ye someone was watching us. Bet they'll turn us in."

Alius shook his head frantically. "No, Ma'am. They'll send us back to the orphanage. You don't have to worry bout us."

"Orphanage, huh? Runaways?"

Nicholas knew his best bet was to be honest. If Lech knew they were nobody of importance, maybe he'd let them go on their way. "Yes, Sir."

"I'll make a deal with ye. Give me what's in those bags and we'll turn a blind eye, we will. Won't turn you in if you forget you've seen us."

Nicholas sighed and cut his eyes toward his friends. He knew they didn't have a chance against the thieves, but he wasn't keen on giving up everything they'd collected.

All at once, a deep growl vibrated through the air. Nicholas jerked his head toward the right as three wolves crept through the snow toward them. Lech stepped back with his hands up in a calming motion.

It did little to calm anyone.

Ula grunted. "What are they doin' hunting in the daylight?"

"Starvin', I imagine," Lech replied. "Nobody move an inch."

The group stilled, praying the pack would move on from disinterest. The large wolf in front stepped forward, intrigued by Alius.

Alius looked close to tears. "He knows I'm meaty," he cried.

The wolf stretched his nose forward and sniffed loudly in Alius's direction. Out of nowhere, Alius screamed louder than any girl he'd ever heard and took off running in the opposite direction of the wolves. If Nicholas had learned one thing about wolves, you should never run away.

"Blimey!" Lech shouted. "Run, Ula!"

Everyone bolted in a different direction, supplies forgotten. Nicholas and Lula followed Alius and watched in fascination as his short arms and legs climbed the nearest tree as if he'd done it a million times.

Pure survival instinct.

Nicholas slid to a stop at the base of the trunk and boosted Lula up the tree toward Alius as fast as he could.

Lech and Ula could still be heard screaming in the forest, followed by the snarls of preying wolves. He ran toward another accessible tree and made it three feet off the ground when sharp teeth snagged the end of his pants, attempting to pull him down. Nicholas kicked while Alius yelled at the beast to get away. Both did little to deter the wolf's grip. Finally, Nicholas hammered one hard kick to its snout, and the wolf whined, shaking off the abrupt hit to the nose. Nicholas climbed quickly to the top of the tree, out of reach.

Howling in the distance pulled the wolf's attention toward the forest and it sprung forward to meet its pack in the woods, giving up on the prey clinging to the tree trunks.

Nicholas exhaled and leaned forward, hitting his head against the bark.

"Thanks for that, Alius," Nicholas said, sarcastically.

"Sorry bout that, Nic." He looked humiliated. "I panicked."

Nicholas couldn't tell if the pink in his cheeks was from running or embarrassment.

"At least they chased the thieves away. We'll keep watch for a bit before we climb down, just to make sure."

Lula nodded, her eyes as wide as saucers. "Good idea."

THE CHILDREN PERCHED LONGER THAN NECESSARY IN THE TALL pines of the forest after the ambush—fearful of hungry thieves and wolves alike. The height from which Nicholas sat offered a different perspective, a reflection if you will. The lush limbs drooped under the weight of the snow, as if carrying a burden those underneath were ignorant of.

How much history had the ancient pines witnessed? Did the forest chuckle, deep and hearty, as it watched the three clueless children wander into the thick of the woods? He imagined they did.

After drinking from the icy creek, the children gathered their supplies and located the road that would lead them to Dalbeca. It wasn't easy, with the new fallen snow attempting to cover their path. Nicholas also worried about the lack of tree cover along the way, leaving them vulnerable and exposed.

They didn't have a choice.

He hoped to arrive in town before nightfall. Especially without the shelter of the train in winter. Nicholas refused to let Alius and Lula freeze—they trusted him to look out for their well-being.

He wouldn't let them down.

The honesty of Tomek's words remained with Nicholas, like a scar on his heart. If he stopped long enough to think of losing the only family he'd ever had, his chest squeezed painfully in fear—a warning to keep them close.

Lula surprised him. She stomped through thick slush, determined to prove her resilience while Alius—their pitiful short-legged friend, brought up the rear, complaining along the way.

"Might we take a rest, Nic?" Alius's labored breaths shook as he fought to speak. "Maybe just a minute." ·

"It's been less than an hour since our last break, Al. If we don't continue, we'll never make it by sunset," Nicholas answered. "Plus, do you really want to risk another run-in with wolves?"

Alius sighed, but didn't reply.

The church was their only hope. Not only for answers he needed, but for food and shelter as well. They'd eaten most of the stale bread and could do with a decent meal. The temperature dropped as the orange glow of sunlight disappeared behind the mountainside, as if whispering goodnight. Nicholas's hands shook as he rubbed his palms together, a feeble attempt to warm his tingling fingertips.

By the time the steep roof of the church peeked the top of the snowy hillside, a collective sigh of relief coursed through the small group, causing haste in their steps.

"I see it! I see it!" Alius shouted.

A single-pointed cross ascended high into the air—a beacon—to lead them where their lives would soon change. Nicholas smiled, gitty at the thought. He'd never been closer to finding out the truth about his family. A sense of comfort rose within him at being so close to his birthplace. Would he love Dalbeca?

Exhaustion forgotten, Alius kept pace with the group and Lula skipped happily through the deep snow. As they drew near, the small down of Dalbeca rose before them. Tall businesses and homes were constructed of a combination of brick and wood, guarding both sides of a narrow cobblestone street. Piles of shoveled snow lined the sidewalks as families hurried out of the brisk winter wind, clutching thick wool coats tight around their neck like lifelines.

Dalbeca was tidy—clean. Small wooden fences surrounded the cottages, controlling pigs and chickens from running free in town. Most of the bushes were trimmed and shaped, and Nicholas imagined how the flower gardens flourished in the spring, blooming pink and green along the sidewalks.

Smoke from old stone chimneys carried the delicious scent of savory spices through the air, and Nicholas's stomach growled in response. Lula clutched the back of his thread-worn jacket, peeking around his shoulder at the curious stares from locals.

"Just act natural. If they suspect something, they might turn us in."

Lula gripped the fabric tighter. "I'm trying, but they're making me nervous."

"Al," Nicholas called out. "Stay close, alright?"

Silence.

"Al?" Nicholas turned, searching.

Alius's long nose pressed against the window of a nearby shop as his tongue swept across his lips.

"Alius! Get over here."

Alius's head jerked away from the bakery window, drool escaping the side of his mouth at the sight of freshly baked pastries. "You ever seen anything like this, Nic?"

"We don't have time for that right now, Alius. Come on," Nicholas ordered, slightly annoyed.

"Alright, alright. You're worse than Berta." Alius

continued to mutter behind them about only wanting a glance of the scrumptious desserts.

Most of the businesses had closed for the evening. Lights flickered and doors were secured as owners made their way home for the night. Most of the stores were basic, selling necessities—bakeries, butchers, a general grocery store.

The orphans shuffled across the stone sidewalk, giving the crowd a wide berth. As they reached the large wooden door of St. Mary's, insecurity kept them frozen in fear. Nicholas clenched his fists.

"Go on, Nic. Knock." Alius shoved Nicholas forward.

"Do you have to knock?" Nicholas asked.

Lula shrugged. "Beats me. We don't have churches like this in Torek."

Nicholas's eyes lowered to the stone front steps. A stark contrast to the comfort of a soft crib offered by loving parents. Such a hard and uncomfortable place to leave a small baby. Did they even care? Did they ever think of him?

Lula's small hand slid into his palm, the gesture warming the bitter loneliness that had taken root. "We're right beside you."

Nicholas swallowed to clear his throat and knocked. They waited, but only the sound of their shaky breaths answered. Nicholas gripped the handle and shoved his weight against the doors, jarring them open. Heat seeped out of the building, wrapping around them like a blanket.

They stepped forward, then jumped as the heavy doors slammed behind them, as if to intimidate them. Nicholas stood in awe with his head tilted toward the ceiling, absorbing the sight of thick overhead rafters and stained glass windows. A musty odor, but not quite unpleasant, surrounded him. A large section of candles sat to his left and rows of pews lined each side of the church.

All was silent.

"Now what do we do?" Lula asked.

Nicholas shook his head. He didn't have a clue.

"Hello?" Alius shouted.

"Shh!" Nicholas scolded, shoving him. "I don't think you're supposed to yell in a place like this, Al."

"Why ever not? Doesn't look like anyone is here." Alius crept toward the candles, inspecting each one with the curiosity of a cat. "Why do you suppose only some are lit? And why are they burning if no one is here? Seems wasteful, if you ask me."

"What a wonderful question," a deep voice murmured from the corner.

Alius jumped, looking up at a tall thin man, dressed in black. As the gentleman took a step forward, Alius tumbled back, righting himself before he fell to the floor.

"Don't be afraid. I'm Father Klimek, the Priest of St. Mary's," he answered with a soft and gentle expression.

Nicholas stepped forward, determination evident in his stiff posture and focused gaze. "I'm Nicholas. This is Alius and Lula."

The priest tilted his head and smiled. "Would you like to sit down?"

Nicholas watched the man intently, searching for any sign of ill intent. There was nothing but a soothing presence that calmed his nerves. He nodded, then the children followed Father Klimek toward the wooden pews in the back. He motioned for them to sit, while he took the pew in front of them, turning to face Alius.

"Now, child. Every lit flame is a symbol of someone's sincere and heartfelt prayer."

The children knew this from their time of prayer with Father Krol, but were only used to a single candle at the orphanage—they'd never seen so many.

"We pray to the angels. The saints. Our Lord above. We confess our sins so that we are worthy of God, our Savior."

The children grew quiet. The priest watched as they took in this information and processed his words.

At once, Alius stood up in a panic. "Lula stole an extra slice of bread at dinner one night!"

"Alius!" Lula shouted.

"You must confess, Lu! You have to! And Nicholas sneaks out of his bed at night when he shouldn't!" Sweat beaded along the top of his forehead from the stress of honesty.

Nicholas lowered his head, embarrassed. "Why are you confessing everyone else's sins, Al? That isn't how it works." His lips tightened from amusement.

Alius glanced up at the priest.

Father Klimek wrinkled his nose and shook his head. "You should confess your own sins and ask for forgiveness, not theirs."

Alius cleared his throat and sat back down. "I'm good." He turned toward Nicholas. "Didn't you have something to ask Father Klimek, Nic? Go on."

Nicholas was taken aback by the sudden change of topic. "Well, yes. If you're finished, Alius."

Alius nodded, clearly uncomfortable.

"Father Klimek, I've come to ask some questions. I hope you can help."

"If I can, of course, Nicholas."

"I've grown up in an orphanage in Torek. The woman who runs the orphanage, Berta, told me I was left here at St. Mary's as a baby. I had hoped someone would remember something about my parents. Anything at all."

Father Klimek's face softened. "You understand we have children dropped at our church at least once a month? We rarely know where they come from."

"Every month?" Lula asked. "That's just awful."

The priest nodded. "It's quite unfortunate. St. Mary's houses one of the largest orphanages in the area, but we've been over capacity for years. We almost always find another orphanage or willing household to take the children. We've been blessed by gracious families in our town."

"Is there any other way to find out?" Lula asked.

"How old are you, Nicholas?"

"Twelve, Sir."

The priest nodded. "I've only been at this parish for a little over eight years, and Alice has worked at the orphanage less than that. It would have been before we arrived. Father Gorski was the leader of St. Mary's during that time and the man has an excellent memory. He might be able to help you."

Nicholas grinned at the possibility.

"I'm not saying he will definitely remember, and he might not be thrilled with the possibility of you showing up on his doorstep. You need to prepare yourself for that."

Nicholas carefully considered his words. He refused to get his hopes up, but if he didn't try, he'd regret it. Thoughts of what-if would forever haunt him. Lula's big brown eyes searched his, waiting for his reply. She nodded her encouragement.

"I'd like to meet Father Gorski," he replied while continuing to meet Lula's gaze.

She grinned.

Alius sighed.

"Where do we find him?" Nicholas asked.

"He retired in a small cottage, not far from town. Maybe a kilometer. It isn't hard to find, but you're welcome to stay the night and leave at sunrise."

As much as Nicholas wanted answers, he and his friends had grown weary. Although not far, the journey had been more than they were accustomed to. "We would be grateful, Father Klimek."

ALICE, A SWEET YOUNG LADY WITH A HUMBLE DEMEANOR, LED the children to a weathered barn behind the church. Two dairy cows and a single horse occupied three of the four stalls inside. Alice opened the door to the fourth, and glanced toward the straw covered ground, as if ashamed.

"It's been hard, finding room for everyone. I'm afraid this is all we have."

Fresh straw lined the floor and thick wood walls and roof protected it against the night air. Nicholas was grateful for the shelter. "Thank you, Alice. This is perfect."

Alice tilted her head at his appreciative nature and handed Lula a stack of blankets and basket of food. Her graceful footsteps made no sound at all as she left the barn, leaving them to their offering for the night.

"Perfect, eh?" Alius asked, turning to stare at the disgruntled horse, snorting in the neighboring stall. He obviously didn't appreciate the company.

"It isn't a tree in the middle of winter, Al. This looks pretty good to me right now."

NICHOLAS ROLLED ON HIS SIDE, ATTEMPTING TO SETTLE IN A more comfortable position on the cold hard ground. Although Alice had brought blankets for comfort, it wasn't as agreeable as the bed he'd grown used to. More than the warmth of the wool throw, he appreciated the water, fish and bread the church had offered.

"Nicholas? Are you awake?" Lula whispered.

Nicholas pushed up on one elbow, peering down toward his feet. "You alright? Do you need anything?" He could barely make out her small silhouette in the dark.

Lula cleared her throat. "Nervous, I guess. This place scares me a little."

"I can understand that. Do you want to move closer?"

Lula nodded, then sat up to lay her head close to his. Alius's soft snores on the hay in front of them echoed throughout the stall.

His thoughts drifted to Berta and the other orphans. What if he failed them? What had Berta thought of him when she realized they had run away? Would she forgive him one day?

They laid quietly for several minutes, but Nicholas could hear her breathing, anxious and uneasy. Still on his right side, he raised his hand toward Lula. She cupped his palm, placing it under her cheek. Her body relaxed and within minutes, fell fast asleep.

Nicholas smiled. He would always be there for her—make her feel at ease.

Protect her.

He would make sure of it.

5

LULA

*L*ula struggled to sit up under the weight of the wool blankets tucked around her shoulders. She wasn't sure at what point during the night her body relaxed in their warmth, but it was probably when Nicholas became cold. He'd tucked his blanket tight around her.

Her heart melted at the sight of him, huddled on his side, asleep. The length of his hair had swept across his brow and she gently pushed it aside. She was only twelve years old. How could she possibly know what love was? She did.

Love held her hand when she was afraid. It warmed her. Fed her. Took care of her like no one else had ever done. Love promised her a future, and she held onto that promise with everything inside of her. She didn't feel twelve—more like twenty. Orphans never had a childhood. They were born taking care of themselves, the harshness of the world visible to their innocent eyes. There was no one to ease them into the suffering of adulthood.

Alius groaned from his position against the wall of their small shelter. He stretched his arms up high, and then a deep rumble vibrated against the wooden planks behind him.

Nicholas jolted awake, eyes wide at the noise. Lula couldn't stop the giggle working its way up her throat.

"It's ok, Nicholas. Alius only let one off," Lula explained.

Nicholas wrinkled his nose and turned his back to Alius. "You're disgusting, Al."

Alius chuckled from across the stall, refusing to reply.

Lula folded up the blankets and piled them into the empty basket. While Nicholas and Alius fought the remnants of sleep, she slipped from the barn to return the kind offerings from St. Mary's.

The church was silent, with only the dim ray of the rising sun beaming through the stained-glass window. A lovely prism of colors bounced around the room, highlighting parts of St. Mary's that she hadn't been able to see the night before.

Her gaze traveled across the wooden-beam design of the ceiling as she walked backward, taking in the smallest of details. All at once, her back hit a hard and unyielding wall. She jumped forward and spun out of fright, dropping the bundle in her arms.

Black pointed shoes, freshly pressed pants, and a long black trench coat covered a thin stick of a man, his head too small for his tall, lanky frame that depended on a cane at his side. His sneer caused his mouth to appear crooked as his thin, greasy hair remained slicked back and firmly in place.

"What are you doing here, girl?" he grumbled.

Lula opened her mouth to speak, but words refused to leave her lips. "I, ah, I," she stuttered.

"Are you ignorant? I asked you a question."

Lula hesitantly raised her head and met his eyes. He took a step back as if struck by a force he didn't anticipate. The hateful man then stumbled forward until he stood inches from Lula's face. The heel of his cane nudged her chin, tilting her face toward the light from the window. His eyes widened.

"Get away from her!" Nicholas shouted.

Nicholas ran into the church and dove in front of Lula. "Don't touch her." His fists balled up at his side in anger and his chest heaved.

The old man chuckled, the evil sound reverberating off the holy walls of St. Mary's. "Who do you think you are, boy?"

"These are my guests, Mr. Brunon." Father Klimek stepped forward. "Now, what is it I can help you with?"

The old man stood straight, eyes focused on Lula. "You there. You know a woman by the name of Betty Sue Dunivant?"

Lula swallowed. She wouldn't tell this horrible man anything. She shook her head. "Never heard of her." Her eyes cut toward Nicholas's concerned gaze. "Time for us to leave."

Nicholas nodded, then turned to where Alius rubbed the sleep from his eyes. "Get our things, Al. We're leaving." Nicholas wrapped his arm around Lula's waist and pulled her toward the door.

Lula knew Nicholas wanted her far away from the creepy bloke. Something about the man scared her, as if his presence was more than a brief altercation. She wanted nothing to do with him.

Father Klimek followed Alius out the front door, a small wrapped bundle in tow. "For your journey." He offered the package to Lula. "It isn't much, but I'm afraid I can't send you off with no reserves. Continue down this street until you reach a path beside the town well. Take that trail until you happen upon a small farm on the outskirts. Father Gorski will be there." The priest smiled. "I will pray for the Lord's blessing on your journey."

"Thank you, Father," Nicholas replied.

The priest nodded. "I must be on my way. Mr. Brunon intends on confessing so I may be in for the long haul."

Father Klimek winked and returned to St. Mary's without another word.

"I might like to be a priest one day," Alius announced while staring at the closed door of the church.

Lula and Nicholas stared at him as if he'd grown a third head.

"Al," Nicholas chuckled. "You tried to confess our sins!"

Alius grumbled at their amusement while pulling his jacket tight around him, stomping toward the well.

The quiet cozy village held an air of mystery that morning. The break in snow left the streets clear of slush and easier to maneuver. Through a small window of a nearby house, Lula watched as a woman stood over a table, busying herself with morning chores. What must it be like to live in such an idyllic town—to raise a family of your own. Lula wanted nothing more than to run her own household. A swarm of children with brown hair and blue eyes and a vegetable garden out back for her family to tend.

"Lula? Are you alright?" Nicholas asked.

She shook off the daydream and smiled. "Yes, of course."

"That man didn't scare you, did he?"

He did. She wouldn't admit it though. "I'm fine, Nicholas."

"Look at those undergarments hanging to dry!" Alius exclaimed. "All for the world to see. Who wants to see their knickers? Not me. I can tell you that."

Nicholas laughed out loud at Alius's rant, but Lula couldn't stop thinking of Mr. Brunon. His dark peering eyes searching for someone he once knew. The recognition terrified her. How did he know her mother?

"That must be the water well up ahead, Al. I see a small path to the right." Nicholas pointed down the cobblestone street to where a round stone-built well sat off to the side.

They were all more quiet than usual. Lula suspected they were deep in thought about how far they'd gone the past few days and what would lie ahead. They followed the snow-covered trail to a small cottage—white with brown wooden trim and a brown shingled roof. Two gigantic trees with heavy evergreen limbs shaded the front of the home with a small wooden wagon sitting underneath, piled with logs.

Alius and Lula stopped several feet from the front door, allowing Nicholas to take the lead. Lula could see the fear in his eyes—the stress of never knowing who he was or where he came from. He stood in front of the door for several seconds before knocking, then took a step back.

The old door, splintering at the sides, scraped against the frame as it opened. An older man, short and heavy, stood in dark brown pants and a white shirt buttoned in the front. There was an air of importance that hovered around him, but a humbleness in his eyes. He looked from one face to another, his brows furrowed in confusion.

"Yes? Can I help you?"

"Are you Father Gorski?" Nicholas asked. He lowered his gaze as if intimidated or nervous.

"That's right," Father Gorski answered. "What can I do for you?"

"Well, Sir. Father Klimek told me you might be able to help me."

The man crossed his arms over his chest and narrowed his eyes. "He did, did he?"

Lula watched Nicholas carefully, concerned at how devastated he would be if the man sent them away.

Nicholas swallowed. "It's about a boy left at St. Mary's, twelve years ago."

Silence.

Father Gorski stepped forward. His glasses sat on the tip of his nose as he tilted his head forward to peer over the rim. "And would that boy find himself on my doorstep today?"

Nicholas nodded. "He would, Sir."

"Look at me, Child."

Nicholas forced his head high and exhaled when the priest's face relaxed. A warmth filled Lula's chest at the sight.

Father Gorski whispered, "I wondered when you'd come see me, Nicholas."

Nicholas gasped. "You, you know me?"

He nodded as his eyes filled with tears. "Come in. We have much to talk about."

One by one, the children followed Father Gorski into the humble cottage. Lula took notice of the plain wood-carved furniture and low ceiling. Simple, with only the necessities. There wasn't a painting on the wall, only a handmade cross hanging above a table with a single lit candle.

The priest led them to a small seating area beside the kitchen and offered fresh water and stew for lunch. Alius's eyes lit up at the steaming bowl before him, a prized possession he might have taken for granted before. He stared as if it would disappear at any moment. As Father Gorski bowed his head to pray, the children followed suit, anxious to savor every bite before them.

A deep moan of satisfaction came from the opposite side of the table as Alius delved into his bowl. Lula's eyes widened at his ill table manners, but the priest only smiled at the enthusiasm. After a few minutes, Nicholas gave in to his curiosity, unable to refrain.

"Who am I, Father Gorski?"

He smiled sadly, as if he knew the questions would come. Father Gorski then stared down at the rough wooden planks of the table without actually seeing them. His mind was on that memorable day—twelve years ago.

"The season had been hard that year. Storms like I'd never seen them. The stained glass of St. Mary's shook from the force of the wind that night, and I feared the cross would rip from the peak of the church."

Father Gorski looked up at Nicholas with downcast eyes, as if the ferocity of the storm confounded him.

"I couldn't sleep, but I don't suppose anyone did that night. I prayed to the heavens above to save us all. There on my knees in the church, with the sound of the wind and swiping limbs against the glass, I heard three knocks against the door of the church."

"What sane man would be out in that storm?" Alius shouted.

Father Gorski smiled. "A fisherman, attempting to secure his boat before he lost his livelihood."

Alius shook his head as if he thought the man had lost his mind.

"Rain pelted down, causing him to trip over a splintered crate sitting on the bank—and that is when he heard the small cry of an infant. The poor soul didn't know what to do, so he rushed to St. Mary's as quickly as possible with the soaked bundle screaming from fear and hunger."

His gaze met Nicholas's. "I remember opening the door to the man's wide eyes as he thrust the bundle into my arms, shouting about what he'd found. But I didn't hear him—not when I pulled the soaked knitted blanket back and met the brightest blue eyes I'd ever seen."

Father Gorski smiled. "We were amazed at God's grace on your life. You were victorious because you have a purpose. Therefore, I named you Nicholas. The people's victory." He met Nicholas's curious eyes. "I struggled to let you go, if I'm being honest. You stayed with us almost a week before Berta accepted you into the orphanage."

"But, why? Why did you struggle?"

"There was something significant about you, as if I was physically holding God's purpose in my hands. I could feel it."

He shook his head, even more confused. "How do I know what my purpose is?"

"Only you and God know the answer to that question. There's something special within you, and I only hope I will be alive to witness the difference you make in the world."

Nicholas shifted in his seat, uncomfortable under the priest's intense scrutiny. "I'm just an orphan, Sir. I want to make a living and support my family. That sounds like plenty of purpose to me."

"A family? Son, you have time to sort that out. You're still young," Father Gorski chuckled.

"No need to sort it. I'll marry Lula, and we're going to have a large family. Right, Lula?"

Lula grinned happily, then threw her hand out toward Father Gorski to display the makeshift ring Nicholas had forged.

Father Gorski tilted his head, peering over his spectacles at her finger. He sat up straight, surprised at the knowledge of their betrothal. "Well, I guess you have it all figured out. Tell me, why the need to know where you came from?"

"Christmas, Sir," Nicholas answered without hesitation.

"Christmas?"

"Yes, Sir. It's a celebration for families and joyous times for children. I want to understand it so I can bring it back to the orphanage. If I don't find my family, how will I ever understand?"

Father Gorski sat back in his chair, as if stunned. "You want to know about Christmas?"

Lula's heart fluttered at the possibility of him telling them everything they needed to know. He could help them understand—bring meaning to it all.

"Yes, please," Lula called out.

"We celebrate the birth of Christ at Christmas. Christ means the anointed One. Jesus was God, come to earth so that we could understand how much God loves us and we would not be afraid to approach Him."

The priest's eyes lit up at the magnificence of their savior. "So," he continued, "The wise men brought gifts to celebrate the birth, therefore we give gifts in remembrance. It's a beautiful celebration of the birth of our Lord."

The children sat frozen, listening intently. They knew he meant well, but it was the same story given by Father Krol. They still didn't understand. Lula was the first to move, nodding fervently as if everything now made perfect sense.

"Thank you, Father Gorski. That was very nice."

A bubble of laughter crept out of Alius at Lula's sincerity, but he covered with a cough. "Excuse me. Yes, very nice indeed."

He nodded, standing from the table as if his work was done. "You three are welcome to stay the night, if you wish. It isn't much, but it's dry and warm. I couldn't put you out in the cold, now could I?"

"Thank you, Sir. That is very kind. Is there something we can help with? To repay you?" Nicholas asked. "We don't want to impose."

The priest scratched the back of his head while he thought it over. "I suppose you could gather more firewood. I split logs earlier and loaded some on the wagon, but my back could use a break."

"Of course. We'll take care of it."

Father Gorski smiled, patted Nicholas on the shoulder and left them to finish their lunch.

"Is anyone any closer to discovering this mysterious joy of Christmas?" Alius asked.

"Not even a little," Nicholas responded.

AFTER LUNCH, LULA CLEARED THE SMALL TABLE AND WASHED the remaining dishes as Nicholas and Alius fetched wood for the fire. She watched from the window as Nicholas carried the heavy load of lumber and Alius supervised every step. She couldn't help but laugh at the sight. Lula dreamt of a cottage such as this, with a small window to watch their children play. One day, she thought. One day...

That night, they huddled together on the hard wood of the floor, warmed by homemade quilts and the orange glow of fire. For the first time since they ran away, they took a moment to appreciate their fortune thus far. They didn't speak, only sat together in comfort. Not hungry. Not cold. And as long as they were together—never alone.

6

NICHOLAS

The next morning, loud, angry voices sliced through their peaceful sleep like a knife. Lula sat up, yawning, then turned her head from side to side as if searching for the ruckus.

"What is that?" she asked.

Nicholas crawled toward the window, peeking out the bottom corner as Alius tucked in close behind him. He held his breath as the hateful man from the church, Mr. Brunon, stood out front—shouting and pointing toward the front door. Two officers, dressed in long dark coats and tall hats, were stationed at his side while Father Gorski remained the ever calm presence and nodded his head in understanding.

Nicholas threw himself to the floor, away from the window. "We have to hide."

"Hide?" Lula asked. "Are we in trouble?"

Alius swallowed, and a bead of sweat broke out across his wide forehead. "It's that mean man, isn't it? What does he want?"

"What mean man?" Lula's shaky voice asked.

"Mr. Brunon." Nicholas answered.

Her face paled, and she looked as though she would cry.

"He may have turned us in, Lu. We have to hide." Nicholas crawled toward the kitchen with Lula and Alius following close behind him. "There aren't many rooms, but maybe the pantry will keep us hidden."

The children piled into the small cupboard together, barely able to close the door before the sound of footsteps echoed across the cottage floor. Nicholas held his breath as his heart pounded against his chest. Several minutes went by, but it felt like hours. Footsteps traveled past their shelter, then returned, stopping directly outside the door. Lula closed her eyes and buried her face on Nicholas's shoulder.

Three small taps on the door—a gentle notion to let them know someone was there. Father Gorski. As the door slowly swung out, the morning light blinded Nicholas as he fought to keep his eyes open. The priest stood over them with his arms across his chest.

"Lula, I need to speak with you, Dear."

Lula refused to face him. She stayed tucked against Nicholas as if Father Gorski would soon give up and go away.

"If you don't go with me, they will come in here after you," he warned.

"Why do they want Lula?" Nicholas asked.

"Is it because I told the priest she stole bread?" Alius asked. "I'll tell them I lied!"

"Lula?" Father Gorski insisted.

Nicholas gripped her hand in comfort. "I'll be with you the whole time. Together? Right?"

Lula nodded. "Together."

One by one, the children shuffled out of the pantry and followed the priest from his cottage. Mr. Brunon sneered at the sight of them, then an evil cackle erupted from his throat. The officers stepped forward and one squatted before Lula.

"Can you tell me your name?" he asked.

"Lula," she answered.

"Lula what?"

Lula cut her eyes toward Mr. Brunon and swallowed. "Lula Faith Dunivant."

Mr. Brunon's greasy smile turned Nicholas's stomach.

The officer nodded. "Lula, I'm going to show you a couple of pictures. Your job is to tell me the truth. Can you do that?"

Lula nodded. Her grip on Nicholas's hand became uncomfortable, and he wished he could do something to help. If only for a few seconds.

The officer showed her a picture of a beautiful red-haired woman, smiling lovingly at the camera. Lula couldn't contain the grin as her eyes lit up."

"That's Mama," she whispered. "It's been so long since I've seen her."

Unable to look away, Lula reached for the photo, but the officer handed over another and Lula's face fell. This time, the beautiful woman's eyes were vacant. The only sign of life was the fierce grip on a small infant at her chest. She held the baby as if someone would rip her away—clutching her as if her life depended on it.

Dark circles lined the woman's heavy eyes, visible in the faded photograph. Behind her stood Mr. Brunon, with one hand gripping her Mother's shoulder. Lula's hands shook as she took a step back.

Nicholas's heart raced at what this meant. It couldn't be.

"I told you she's mine! That woman took her from me years ago!" Mr. Brunon shouted for the whole town to hear, as if he needed a witness.

"Now, Mr. Brunon. You're scaring the child. She has no idea who you are," Father Gorski stated. "Let's all calm down and talk to Lula in a civilized manner."

The officer nodded. "I agre . . ."

"Give her to me! You can't keep my kid away from me any longer. She belongs to me!" Mr. Brunon stepped forward and Nicholas rushed in front of Lula.

"I told you to never touch her," Nicholas yelled.

"I tire of your disrespect, child. Get out of my way."

Alius stepped up on the other side, protectively.

Father Gorski's hand covered Nicholas's right shoulder as he leaned down to whisper. "There's a time to fight a man like him for what is right. Today isn't that day, Nicholas. He'll turn you over to the orphanage and you'll be further from Lula."

Nicholas peered down into Lula's big brown eyes. He palmed the side of her face as hot tears ran down her cheeks. "We'll be together again."

"Promise?" she asked.

"I promise."

Mr. Brunon shoved past the crowd surrounding Lula, then gripped her by her upper arm. "Time to go home."

"You're hurting me!" Lula cried.

The police stepped forward as though they wanted to stop him, but had no right to keep him from his own child. Lula's feet kicked against the dry snow as she cried, pulling away from the stranger that claimed to be her father.

"No! I don't want to go! Please! I'll go back to the orphanage. Please don't let him take me away! Nicholas! Alius! Please, I need you!"

Nicholas ran forward, but was quickly halted by an officer on each side. He fought his way to Lula, but it was no use. As big as he was, he wasn't as strong as the officers. "Please do something!" he shouted.

One officer removed his tall, thick hat and tilted Nicholas's head back to look at him. "I would if I could. I give you my word. Father Gorski is right. Today is not the day."

"I have to get her back. I'm supposed to protect her."

The officer's face softened. "I believe you, but there's nothing we can do."

Nicholas watched until he could no longer see her blonde hair whipping in the wind or hear the icy terror in her voice. Hours passed as his feet went numb from the frigid snow. His chest fought to breathe in the cold winter air, but Alius never left his side. Nicholas felt as though someone had stolen a piece of his heart that day.

"Nicholas? Come inside, Son. There's nothing you can do out here except catch a fever." The priest stood at the door, waiting patiently.

Alius tugged at his arm, forcing him into the shelter of the cottage. Nicholas contained the urge to hit him. Alius. Father Gorski. Mr. Brunon. He wanted to fight them all. The priest covered Nicholas's shoulders with a heavy blanket and sat him down in front of the fire.

"I know this is confusing, but Lula is strong. Both of you will get through this."

Nicholas raised his head to meet his eyes. "I may be young, Father Gorski, but even I know a wife wouldn't run away from her husband unless she was afraid. Not with a young child. That tells me what kind of man he is."

The priest's face fell and his eyes held a sadness he tried to conceal.

"I will get her back," Nicholas promised.

"Not today, though. You need rest. I'm going to round up something for us to eat." He walked toward the kitchen, then stopped to look over his shoulder. "You and Alius are welcome to stay one more night if you'd like. Get your head on straight. I could always use an extra hand."

Alius nodded. "Thank you, Father Gorski."

His mouth pulled up on one side, and he disappeared into the other room.

Alius fell to his knees in front of Nicholas. "Nic, what are we going to do? We can't let Lu stay with that man. Did you see his eyes? He's a lunatic!"

Nicholas's gaze never left the roaring flames of the fire as it danced inside the stone structure. His mind scoured every avenue, every conceivable option. The truth seeped into his heart and squeezed, a pain that kept his lungs from expanding and his mind from focusing. He was nothing but a child. No power. No knowledge—and he'd lost the most precious thing in his life.

"NICHOLAS, I NEED TO RUN INTO TOWN. WOULD YOU AND Alius like to go?"

Alius glanced up from clearing the brush outside the cottage. He looked over his shoulder at Nicholas, waiting for his reply. Nicholas hadn't seen Lula since the day Mr. Brunon had taken her weeks before, and this could be his opportunity. He knew it was a slim chance, but it was better than nothing.

"Yes, Sir. We'll be glad to go with you." Nicholas cut his eyes toward Alius, and his friend nodded in agreement.

None of them had spoken of their arrangement, but it appeared Father Gorski was glad to let them stay as long as they were making themselves useful. Nicholas and Alius were grateful. They continued making plans to locate Alius's family, but they wouldn't leave without Lula. She belonged with them—not Mr. Brunon.

Every day, less snow fell. That, along with the hard frozen ground, offered an accessible path into town. As soon as Nicholas stepped onto the cobblestone street, his gaze traveled across every house—every window for any sign of her.

Father Gorski led the boys into an old general store, with dusty hardwood floors. An older man, wearing a white apron with his gray hair parted on the side, greeted the priest warmly. Nicholas and Alius shuffled around the store, absorbing the trinkets and pantry items on the shelves before them.

Nicholas strolled along the rows, until something caught his attention. Through the shelving, on the other side of the aisle, were the biggest brown eyes he'd ever seen. Eyes he dreamt of when he fell asleep at night.

Lula.

He stepped forward and his nails bit into the edge of the wooden shelf. His grip became painful, but he didn't seem to care.

"Lula," he whispered. "Are you alright?"

She looked from side to side, as if afraid she'd be caught. She didn't answer his question. "I miss you and Alius. I want to go home."

"We're going to get you out of there. I promise. Stay strong, Lula."

Alius caught up to Nicholas, and his eyes widened at the sight of her. "Awe, Lu." His chin quivered as if he were on the verge of tears. "We're still at Father Gorski's cottage. If you can get away, that's where you'll find us."

Her soft whisper broke Nicholas's heart. "He'll never let me go. Never."

"We're going to run away together, Lula. Just like we planned. We'll get out of here and never come back." Nicholas promised.

She swallowed and started to speak, but a gravelly voice rang throughout the store, interrupting her. "What are you doing over there, Girl?"

Lula bowed her head in submission as a black cane swiped through the air and poked her in the back of the neck—pushing her toward the exit. The boys watched as he forced Lula out the door, crying. Nicholas balled his fists and stepped forward, but Alius held tight to the back of his coat.

"It has to be the right time, Nicholas. Like Father Gorski said."

"It's been a month, Alius. How long do you want her to stay there?"

Alius shook his head, frustrated. "Not another minute. But I also don't want Lu punished because you don't think things through. Can you imagine what he would do? Be smart, Nic. That's all I'm tryin' to tell ya."

"Boys? I need help at the front," Father Gorski called out.

Nicholas attempted to close off the anger fueled by his helplessness. The store owner threw a large sack of flour and a bag of potatoes at their feet.

"I'm afraid my winter stock is quite bare. We're fortunate it's lasted this long."

"The Lord provides," the priest responded. "We must be off."

Nicholas hoisted the flour on one shoulder while Alius fought with the sack of potatoes. Father Gorski held several other items in his arms as they left the store and made their way back home.

He debated staying silent, but Nicholas trusted the priest to be honest with him. "How does God feel about anger?"

He glanced down with his brows pulled together in confusion. "Where did that come from?"

Nicholas shrugged. "Just something I've been thinking about."

"God wants you to forgive your fellowman. If you truly forgive, you won't be angry." He peered over at Nicholas with a smirk. "Of course, you are also human and not expected to be perfect. That's why our God forgives."

Alius chuckled. "Thank goodness. Nicholas is angry enough for the both of us."

"Mind your business, Al," Nicholas mumbled.

"Do you want to share why you are so angry? It helps."

Nicholas walked in silence for a few seconds, trying to determine the reasons he felt as he did. "I guess, I'm angry because I don't have a family. I'm angry that I've never experienced Christmas, not like most people. Mad because Lula is held hostage by her own father and I can't do anything to help her."

Father Gorski nodded. "All valid reasons. But I think your feelings are more from sadness and helplessness than anger. Mr. Brunon is an angry man, Nicholas. Do you see the difference?"

"I guess so. I feel angry, though."

"You're protective. Fierce. Loving. There is little hostility in you unless you are attempting to right a wrong. Your aggression comes from a place of love."

Nicholas absorbed the priest's words, swallowing the large lump in his throat. He hoped he was right. The last thing he wanted was to be like Mr. Brunon.

. . .

THAT NIGHT, NICHOLAS LAID ON HIS BLANKET ON THE FLOOR, thinking about the man he wanted to become. Honest. Faithful. Dependable. Not someone whose wife would want to run away. What happened in that house for her to leave with a small child? Whatever the reason, Nicholas saw her as brave—fierce, like his Lula.

"Hey, Nic?"

"Yes, Alius?"

"Don't laugh, but I made you something today."

Nicholas pushed up on his elbows, peering over at the blush across Alius's cheeks, lit by firelight. "I won't laugh."

Alius took a deep breath and pulled a small wooden doll from under the blanket, carved from a knife. Intricate crevices had been sliced in a whimsical design for her long hair, and the round-hooded eyes and plump upper lip portrayed her perfectly. The head of the doll was larger than the body, as her hands clenched together at chest level. He knew without asking—it was Lula.

Alius bowed his head, as if embarrassed. "You've been so sad. I thought it might make it easier if you had something to remember her by."

Nicholas didn't know what to say, and he feared he'd cry if he tried to speak. His hand clamped down on Alius's shoulder, and he smiled. Alius grinned, then turned on his side to sleep. Father Gorski had told them to be patient, devise a plan and play it smart. Mr. Brunon wasn't a man to take lightly, and he would keep a close watch on Lula. Nicholas stared at the doll's face and swore nothing would stand in his way of rescuing her.

Nothing.

7

LULA

Six Months Later

*L*ula stretched her back, sore from the position on her knees as she scrubbed every inch of the hard floor with the small, frayed brush. The planks of wood left indentions in the skin of her knees, black and blue from hours of scrubbing. She squeezed her hands to alleviate the cramps, but nothing helped. It had been an hour—maybe two since he'd allowed her to stand, and if he caught her stretching, she'd be in for it.

The last thing she wanted to do was anger him.

It wasn't a large place by any means, and the limited furniture made it easier to keep clean than if it was cluttered. A wood-burning heater sat in the center of the room with an exhaust pipe traveling to the roof. A wooden bench that reminded her of the pews at St. Mary's sat for looks, but was never used. Both he and Lula retired to their own rooms after dinner, uninterested in conversation.

Lula knew the only reason he forced her to stay was to take care of him as he aged—he'd said as much. He didn't care for her, and she doubted he had ever loved her mother. She couldn't imagine him loving anyone.

Mr. Brunon, as he instructed her to call him, was particular about his house. She knew to spend an hour everyday on the flooring. When she finished early one particular morning, he became unhinged, accusing her of being lazy and ungrateful. She wanted to remind him she never asked to live there, but she kept her mouth shut. She always did.

It was the longest six months of her life. She had watched the last of the snow melt and bright green sprouts of grass appear, as if signaling a new beginning. But not for her. Her life was over. She'd found herself in a pit of darkness with no way out. Mr. Brunon would never allow her to dream of a future—not as long as he was around.

She started early every morning, cooking the first of three meals. Lula struggled in the beginning. Learning to cook at the age of twelve with no instruction wasn't easy. The first swipe across her face came after she burned his eggs. The vision in her right eye blurred for two days after. She never overcooked anything again.

The next time he hit her, was after she poked herself with a sewing needle, staining his pants with a drop of her blood. Lula had never held a needle before, but quickly learned what she needed to do to keep from getting whipped.

Ever since the incident at the general store, Mr. Brunon refused to let her out of the house. Except for tending the garden, she wasn't allowed to go anywhere or speak to anyone. She'd taken to singing in the quiet, solitary moments when he was in town. Mainly lullabies she'd heard as a child, or sometimes she would make up her own lyrics, full of sadness and longing. She hated the depressed soul she had become.

After meals were cooked, and the cold, small house sparkled, she would climb up to the enclosed loft above the kitchen and sit beside the window. She imagined Nicholas and Alius running through the fields as the sun dimmed behind the distant mountainside. Determined to rescue her from this prison, they would climb high to her window to free her, leaving this nightmare behind.

Had they celebrated Easter like always? Did they have bread and honey for breakfast like Alius loved? Did anyone bake pierniki as Berta did? Did Nicholas think of Lula as often as she did him? She twisted the small ring constructed of wire around her finger and grinned.

Yes. She knew he did.

"You brush every square inch of that floor, Girl?"

"My name is Lula," she mumbled.

"What did you say to me?"

"I said I'm almost finished," she called out sweetly.

He wrinkled his nose at her reply. "That's what I thought. Snarky like Betty Sue—that's what you are."

Lula paused the circular motion of the brush at her mother's name.

"Spoiled and selfish. The biggest mistake of my life, she was." Mr. Brunon hobbled into his room, grumbling along the way. Before shutting the door, he shouted over his shoulder. "Have my dinner ready or else!" The little house shook from the force of the door slamming shut.

Lula exhaled at the relief of being alone again. When the rumble of his snore could be heard from the bedroom, she crept toward the corner desk, opening the bottom right-side drawer to pull out the antique box she knew would be there. Every moment she could spare, she dove into the memories, clinging to every detail.

Pictures of her mother, heirlooms, and jewelry . . . it was all there. Sentimental items that every young woman hoped to be able to hand down to their daughter one day. She'd found it while dusting the roll-top desk one afternoon, but placed it back before he realized how much it meant to her. If he knew, he'd burn it.

She knew which ring was her mother's wedding band based on the photos in the box. Lula wanted nothing to do with it. But the gold band with deep red garnet and emerald stones across the top—there was something about that one. Just like every other time, she placed it on her finger and closed her eyes, the connection she felt to her mother warming the chill within.

She didn't know how long she sat, absorbed in her mother's memories, but the scraping of Mr. Brunon's cane on the hardwood snapped her from her daze. She scrambled to place everything back inside. Wiggling the drawer, she shoved it flush against the desk as he limped back into the room. He paused, his eyes traveling over every square inch of space as if he searched for a reason to scold her.

"What are you doing down there?" One brow raised, suspicious.

"I missed a place in the corner. Just making sure everything is spotless before dinner, Sir."

Lula pushed off her knees and hurried toward the kitchen, but Mr. Brunon stepped directly in her path. With the butt of his cane, he tilted her chin up and peered over her features, one by one. Her eyes, nose, lips . . .

"So much like her. Except the fair head. Your mother was a red-head. Where do you suppose that came from?" He tilted his head in thought. "If I ever find out you aren't mine, I'll have no use for you. Do you understand?"

Lula's mouth went dry at the threat. "Yes, Sir."

Mr. Brunon stepped around her, the forceful brush of his shoulder knocking her back a step.

What would he do to her? Would he kill her for the embarrassment? She didn't think it would be as easy as putting her on the street—that would be a blessing. Deep inside, there was little doubt he was her father. She knew her mother would have never married him unless forced—she knew that with all of her heart.

Betty was a pure soul, filled with love and honesty. Even as nasty as he was, she wouldn't have betrayed her vows to him unless she feared for Lula's life. She wasn't sure how she knew this, but she did.

Lula stood at the uneven wooden table, pulling potatoes out of the sack to chop for dinner. Glancing out the small windowsill, she watched as Mr. Brunon took his usual afternoon stroll up the sidewalk. She imagined him fussing at the children and complaining about the neighborhood chickens —per usual.

She continued chopping potatoes, taking extra care each cube was identical in size and shape, just the way he liked. The thin, fine hair on the back of her neck stood at attention and the feeling of being watched caused her hands to freeze in place.

Looking over her shoulder, her gaze traveled around the room, but she was alone. Lula shook her head, convinced she'd lost her mind. Then, something caught her attention outside the window. Behind the shrubbery, to the left of the property, stood Nicholas. His frame, larger than she remembered, crouched low as he watched her with eyes full of sadness.

She didn't think. Lula dropped the knife and dashed out the front door, needing to see his face, if only for a minute. Mr. Brunon was nowhere in sight, but Lula busied herself, pulling weeds from the flowers, as she made her way toward the bushes.

"Nicholas," she whispered. "What are you doing here?"

He smiled. "I looked up from the street and saw the most beautiful face I'd ever seen through a window. Like an angel."

She shook her head as if he were ridiculous. "You know you can't be here."

"I know. I just wanted to see you, if only for a few minutes. Father Gorski is waiting for me."

"It's wonderful to see you." Lula wanted to wrap her arms around him, just like she always had, but she was afraid.

"I haven't given up, Lula. Me and Alius, we've been making plans. I want you to know that."

She grinned a half smile and turned to look over her shoulder—running directly into Mr. Brunon. Lula staggered back, but his hand around her throat kept her from falling. He pulled her delicate face to his and hissed, "You aren't supposed to leave my house without permission. Isn't that right?"

Lula nodded, terrified of what would come next.

"I apologize, Sir. I was just saying hello. Didn't mean to intrude," Nicholas called out.

Mr. Brunon never spared him a glance, but released her throat only to backhand her to the ground. Nicholas jumped from the shrubs and crouched beside Lula.

"Lula? Are you alright?"

"Get away from her!" Mr. Brunon shouted.

"I'm, I'm okay. You should go, Nicholas."

Nicholas shook his head. "I can't leave you."

"I'll give you one more chance, Boy. Get off my property."

"Come with me, Lula," he whispered.

Before Lula could answer, Mr. Brunon's cane flew through the air, crashing against the side of Nicholas's head. He fell to his side and Lula feared he'd blacked out. Before he could stand, a pointed black boot kicked his ribs, and he cried out from the impact. Nicholas gasped for air.

Lula screamed for Mr. Brunon to stop, but he was relentless—insisting on teaching the boy a lesson. Nicholas couldn't catch his breath as the cane swiped across his face once again. Tears ran down Lula's cheeks at the sight of Nicholas, battered and bleeding, all for the sake of what? Her? No, she wasn't worth his suffering.

A deep rumble of authority rang out along the street as everyone within earshot froze in place. The cane was ripped from Mr. Brunon's hand, then thrown across the yard. Father Gorski fell to the ground beside Nicholas.

"Are you mad?" The priest wrapped his arm around Nicholas and helped him to his feet. "He is only a boy!"

Mr. Brunon narrowed his eyes. "That boy will learn to respect me!"

Father Gorski sighed. "God help you, Mr. Brunon. God help your soul."

Mr. Brunon pointed toward the house, a silent demand for Lula to get inside. She glanced toward the priest and saw nothing but pity in his eyes.

"Lula." Mr. Brunon shouted.

Had he ever used her name? She didn't think so. Lula stood on shaky legs and concentrated on putting one foot in front of the other, as if she'd forgotten how to walk. She glanced back as Father Gorski fought to keep Nicholas upright, as if he'd topple at any moment.

Father Klimek ran out of St. Mary's, aiding the former priest. Curious residents of Dalbeca gathered in the street, noisily peering into the yard of the crazy man they typically avoided at all costs.

Mr. Brunon shouted at the top of his lungs for all to hear. "You think I'm afraid of you self-righteous men who claim to know God? You are not worthy, just like anyone else. If you want to do some good in this world, maybe you should instill respect within our children! That's what they need!" he called out.

Father Klimek led the others inside the church, and all Lula wanted to do was follow. She needed to see Nicholas.

To know he was alright. At that moment, the smart decision was to walk straight back to the kitchen and continue chopping potatoes as if it never happened. At least she would have a knife in her hand.

That's exactly what she did. Lula's hands shook as she gripped the vegetable. What was this man capable of? She closed her eyes, attempting to gain control, but all she could see was Nicholas's battered face. At the sound of the front door, she cleared her throat and relaxed her shoulders—a weak attempt to look unphased. When Mr. Brunon stomped into the kitchen, his gaze took in the blade. Then he narrowed his beady eyes on her face.

"What did you think you were doing out there?"

"I needed fresh air, so I decided to pull weeds from the flower beds. Nicholas spotted me and stopped to say hello."

"You expect me to believe that?"

She ignored his question. "I must get back to dinner if it's going to be ready in time. Please excuse me," she answered.

He huffed and puffed his way back toward the main room, peeking out the window toward the church every so often in case they came back. She had a feeling he hoped they did.

8

NICHOLAS

"What were you thinking?" Father Gorski asked between cleaning the gashes across Nicholas's face. "You know it isn't safe for you or her. The man is mad."

"He's right. Mr. Brunon has serious issues. Look at what happened today," Father Klimek mumbled, as he accepted the clean cloth from Alice. "He is her father, Nicholas. The officers won't do anything to him, but they will punish you."

Nicholas winced from the stinging sensation across his cheek. He wished Alius were there. He'd stayed at the cottage to finish weeding Father Gorski's vegetable garden. His heart hurt for Lula and every time he closed his eyes, he saw Mr. Brunon strike her. Did she endure that every day?

Father Gorski paused and stared at Nicholas. "Truly. What were you thinking?"

Nicholas teared up as he fought to keep his emotions hidden. "It's been six months since I've seen her. It feels like years. When I caught sight of her through the window, I couldn't walk away. I couldn't."

Father Gorski cut his eyes toward Father Klimek and

grinned. He exhaled, leaning back in his seat. "Was it worth it?"

Nicholas sincerely thought about the question. "It was until he hit her. I can't take it, Father Gorski. I have to get her out of there."

The priest exhaled through his nose and sat back. He pursed his lips at Nicholas's words. "Do me a favor. Don't tell me what your plan is. If the authorities come knocking on my door, you know I won't lie, Son. Just don't tell me."

"Yes, Sir."

"WE'RE DOING WHAT?" ALIUS ASKED. "HAVE YOU SEEN YOUR face? Do you really want to go back there?"

"Do you want to leave Lula there? Is that what you want?"

Alius bowed his head, ashamed of his outburst. "Of course not, Nic."

Nicholas knew Alius cared for Lula, but he couldn't allow his fear to keep him from rescuing her. "I'm going to collect supplies and come up with a plan. I'll be leaving this week, so you need to decide if you're coming with us." Nicholas stood to walk inside the house.

"You know I'm always with you. No matter what," Alius whispered.

Nicholas didn't turn around, but paused. He closed his eyes at Alius's words, thankful for their friendship. He nodded once and walked through the back door of the cottage.

Nicholas found Father Gorski, sitting in an old rocking chair with a Bible in hand—his afternoon ritual. He took a moment to watch the man who'd been there during some of the most trying times in his life. He hated to say goodbye, but this wasn't where he belonged. Nicholas couldn't be sure how he knew, but he did.

"Is there a reason you're spying on me?" Father Gorski called out.

Nicholas leaned against the doorframe and crossed his arms over his chest. "You said we could stay one night," Nicholas whispered.

"Pardon?"

"One night. That's what you said the first day we met. You said we could stay for the night. But you've never asked us to leave."

Father Gorski closed his Bible and smiled. "You've never given me a reason to."

"I'm serious."

"I am, too." He sat the Bible on the small table beside his chair and leaned forward, clasping his hands in front of him. "What's wrong, Nicholas?"

He met his gaze, surprised by how steady his voice sounded as emotion overwhelmed him. "I don't know how to say goodbye."

Father Gorski looked away from Nicholas, unable to keep eye contact. "Do you feel as though you must?"

"I do. I will honor the promise I made you. You won't know when or where we're going. It's important to me you know how much we appreciate your kindness. I'm not sure what we would've done."

The priest swallowed before he spoke, fidgeting in his chair. "From the first time I laid eyes on you, I knew God had his hand on your life. You have a purpose, greater than anything I could offer you here. Knowing I had a short time with you on your journey makes me incredibly grateful. To be a small part of your life, I thank God for that every night." Father Gorski blinked tears from his dark eyes, and took a deep, shuddering breath.

Nicholas walked across the planks of the floor, the creak of old wood slicing through the quiet sadness consuming them. He fell to his knees in front of Father Gorski with his hands clasped in front of him. The priest placed his hand on his head, praying over Nicholas and the journey that awaited. He prayed for the future of all three of them, the people that would be forever changed by their presence, and protection over their lives.

There was freedom, an uplifting warmth, when you gave yourself over to God. As if no matter what took place, it would eventually lead to a road with purpose and meaning. Nicholas clung to that hope.

TWO NIGHTS LATER, NICHOLAS AND ALIUS CREPT AROUND THE cottage, stuffing their potato sacks with belongings they'd brought from the orphanage. Although Father Gorski had obviously left additional fruits and vegetables on the counter, a generous offering, they refused to take anything else from the selfless man they had grown to love. He'd given enough.

After they packed, Nicholas stood in the center of the room, taking in the cottage one last time before leaving it behind. It was a bittersweet moment, one he'd never expected to find himself in when he arrived on the doorstep of the priest.

"Nic, time to go." Alius stood by the door—short stubby arms wrapped around his bag as he struggled to peek over the top.

Nicholas followed him out the door as the dark, humid night enveloped him. Summer at the cottage carried lovely notes of fresh cut grass and ripe strawberries, and he would forever reminisce on his time here whenever the scent sparked a memory. Just as the smell of musty books and raspberry tea leaves reminded him of Berta.

There was no way to warn Lula of their plan. It was too risky. Alius's slight legs had struggled to keep up on the voyage to Dalbeca, and he didn't want him falling behind, so Alius would travel to the fisherman's wharf to wait for Nicholas and Lula.

They would have to take a boat. Not a large fisherman's vessel, but a small canoe or paddle boat, washed up on the bank after a storm. Father Gorski had told them stories about the old boats on the wharf after giving Nicholas the details of being found nearby. The priest had said there were always plenty of abandoned canoes, but few were in good enough shape to hold up on the Baltic Sea.

Nicholas hoped he was wrong. He didn't stop to think of a plan, mainly for fear of backing out—realizing he was in over his head. All he could think of was Lula. How would he free her from Mr. Brunon's grasp?

As the worn path turned into cobblestone streets, Nicholas turned toward Alius and sighed. "This is where we part, Al."

"Hey, Nic? I'm not sure this is the best time to bring it up, but I don't believe I can do this."

"Do what?"

"Any of it. Find the wharf, secure a boat. Have you met me, Lad?"

"I have faith in you, Al." Nicholas slapped him on the back and smiled, although he wasn't confident in his short, self-conscious friend. Alius had a way of overthinking the smallest details, which usually stood in his way of the ultimate goal.

"Do your best, Al. I'll be right behind you and we'll figure out the rest together. Alright?"

"Yeah." Alius sighed, then shuffled toward the other side

of the cobblestone street toward the sea. He'd only have maybe half a mile to walk from what Father Gorski had told them. He looked over his shoulder once more, his teary eyes full of fear and sadness. "Be waitin' on you."

Nicholas hoisted his bag and took off toward Mr. Brunon's house. The streets were silent, and void of the usual spicy aroma wafting through the air. The summer breeze that usually blew through his hair had vanished and the loud chirping of birds overhead fell silent. As if the town froze to watch him, curious about his intentions. At once, a deep roar of thunder ran across the sky and a light rain ran down his forehead. Then Nicholas realized—that was his calm before the storm.

He stalled several times and peeked over his shoulder, expecting dark shadows to be following. He knew his anxiety would continue to get the best of him if he didn't focus. The old cottage sat ahead on the right, across from St. Mary's. The overgrown bushes out front and splintered wood around the windows gave it away.

Nicholas dropped his bag beside the shrubs and crept along the wall of the house. Thankfully, there was an absence of windows on that side of the neighbor's cottage, so he didn't fret about being seen. He couldn't be sure where Lula slept, so he hoped to get a better view through a back window or door.

As Nicholas rounded the corner of the house, the back door flung open—slamming against the wood siding.

"If you know what's good for you, you'll have that mess cleaned up by the time I return!"

Nicholas dove toward the ground, flattening himself in the wet grass against the side of the house. The door slammed closed and Mr. Brunon hobbled out on his cane, mumbling about the girl's ignorance. He stared up toward the sky, as if evaluating the approaching storm, then shook his head and continued on. The tip of the cane swept the grass a couple of inches from Nicholas's face and he held his breath, trying not to move.

He waited until Mr. Brunon crossed the street toward St. Mary's and crawled along to the back of the house toward the door. He gripped the handle tightly, as beads of sweat coated his neck. The door frame whined, but finally relented as Nicholas forced the latch loose.

He stepped into the cottage, the smell of ammonia overpowering anything that Lula had cooked that night. What mess was Mr. Brunon referring to? How often did she clean? Nicholas shook his head and peeked into the small, bare kitchen. Empty.

A wood-burning heater and wooden bench sat empty in the main room. Where could she be? His gaze traveled up the wooden steps to a loft and before he knew it, his feet followed. Every step groaned under his weight, but he didn't have the luxury of time—he needed to hurry.

The enclosed loft came into view as he topped the stairs. A straw mattress sat awkwardly on the floor next to a window. That was it. Lula stood at the window brushing her hair, in a world of her own. He imagined her thinking of their life together—in some far off land. He grinned and took a few seconds to watch her.

"Lula?"

She spun, dropping the brush and throwing her hand over her chest. "Nicholas? What are you doing here? Oh, my. Your face looks horrible! I'm so sorry!"

Nicholas hurried across the room and wrapped her in his arms. "I'm fine. Look, we need to get you out of here. He could return any minute."

"But, where?"

"Not here. Somewhere far from Dalbeca. Al is waiting for us."

Lula dropped her head, her eyes focused on the floor away from the intensity in Nicholas's. Once again, she was afraid.

"Lula, we have to try. You can't stay here."

Her eyes teared up, but whether it was from fear or excitement, he couldn't be sure. She bit her bottom lip as if to keep it from quivering.

"Alright, Nicholas. Let's go."

His shoulders sagged from relief. "Find your boots, quickly."

Lula clumsily pushed her arms through coat sleeves, while attempting to shove her feet into her worn boots at the same time. She left everything else. As Nicholas and Lula reached the bottom step, the back door swung open. Nicholas could hear Mr. Brunon grumbling about the priest as the door slammed shut.

He tiptoed underneath the steps of the loft as Lula followed. It wasn't much of a hiding spot, but the tiny cottage allowed for nothing else. Mr. Brunon limped to the center of the room, and his chin lifted as his eyes cut from side to side. He suspected something—Nicholas knew it.

"Girl! Where are you?"

Lula shook all over.

"Get down here, right now!"

Nicholas knew Mr. Brunon terrified her. Lula clenched her fists and kept her eyes trained on the floor, refusing to look his way. Was she afraid she would relent? Mr. Brunon stepped toward the stairs, toward the loft, and stretched his lanky neck as if he could see her sitting by the window.

One, two, and three steps—the cane slammed down on the wooden slat in front of Nicholas's face. His lungs burned from the breath he held, and he closed his eyes as if he could ignore the evil old man standing above him. As Mr. Brunon reached the top step, Nicholas grabbed her hand and snuck around the stairs to make their escape.

A shocked gasp from Mr. Brunon echoed around the small cottage in Lula's absence. He spun to see the children running toward the door and threw his cane in the air—shouting in anger.

"This will be the last time you disrespect me, Boy!"

Mr. Brunon hurried after Nicholas and Lula, but missed the step and tumbled down the wooden stairs, awkwardly to the floor. Lula's feet faltered as if she would go back, but Nicholas jerked her out the door, knowing what he would do when he got up.

"Nicholas, what if he's badly injured?"

"It's now or never. What will he do to you after he gets up, Lula? Do you want to find out?"

Lula shook her head while tears rolled down her cheeks.

Thunder continued to roll as summer rain gently poured overhead. "We need to run, Lu. Stay with me. Alright?"

Her chest heaved as her slight frame shook from fright. Lula's head nodded in agreement, more quickly than she probably intended.

Nicholas bolted toward the street to grab his bag. Then the clomp of their boots hitting the wet cobblestone bricks was the only sound in the night. As they reached the path on the left that Alius walked down minutes before, a collection of loud whistles alarmed the small town of crime in their midst. No doubt—they were the criminals. Mr. Brunon was obviously uninjured, and had reached the officers to report Lula's disappearance.

They ran faster, legs burning from the stress of their heavy boots pounding against the hard terrain. The storm continued to increase in intensity and he squinted against the pelting rain. The pounding of horse hooves were not far behind as shouts of alarm could be heard throughout the town.

What would they do to them if caught? What would happen to Lula?

"I can't keep up, Nicholas. I don't think I can do this!"

Nicholas slowed to Lula's pace, wrapping his free arm around her lower back. "You can do it, Lu. I know you can."

Nicholas could hear the crashing waves in the distance. They were close. White sails of fishing boats were barely visible in the dim moonlight covered by storm clouds. They swayed back and forth in the wind as the salty smell of ocean water filled his nose with every deep breath.

They arrived at the wharf, but struggled to find Alius in the rain. Nicholas didn't want to shout and give away their location, so they searched every dock until his short stocky frame came into view beside the water. Standing by an abandoned paddle boat, he jumped up and down—waving frantically.

"Hurry! I see lanterns over there! Hurry, Nic!" Alius shouted.

Nicholas threw his bag into the boat and held out his hand for Lula to climb inside. Nicholas and Alius shoved against the heavy wood of the canoe, burrowed deep in place from settling.

"Hey! You there! Stop this instant!" An authoritative voice belted from the trees, running toward the children.

Nicholas pushed once more—freeing the boat from its burrow into the rough waves of the sea. He summoned all of his strength, mind and body, to force the vessel past the whitecaps as the storm beat against his face. Just as he dove into the boat, Alius gripped his arms and pulled with all his might.

Consumed with seeing Nicholas safely inside the boat, the children never noticed the officer running down the dock on their left—not until it was too late. The man jumped from the end of the dock, landing feet from their only chance at freedom. Nicholas and Alius both grabbed for the paddles, attempting to speed away from the man swimming toward them. It was no use.

As soon as the officer threw one hand on to the side, the other wrapped around Lula's wrist and jerked her halfway off the boat. Nicholas dove for her ankle, refusing to let her go.

He wouldn't fail her again.

He pushed and pulled as Lula cried out in pain and fear. She hit the man with her free hand and screamed for him to release her.

"Please! Please leave me alone!" she cried.

The sound of her agonized voice was torture. Alius picked up a paddle, swinging it above his head as if to hit the officer in the face. Before he could, the man tugged once more, pulling Lula's small body overboard into the murky black depths of the water.

Time slowed—the devastating image of Lula's blonde hair spread underneath the water forever burned into his brain. Her big brown eyes opened slowly as if needing to see his face once more. The officer jerked her toward the surface and it snapped Nicholas from his daze.

"Lula! No!" Nicholas stepped forward to jump in after Lula. An arm wrapped around his waist, fighting to keep him on board.

"Look, Nic!" Alius pointed toward the dock where three other officers had dove in and were attempting to swim toward them. "We'll never get her back. Not tonight. If we don't get out of here, we'll be locked away for good."

Nicholas's gaze traveled across every man in the water, then his gaze landed on a set of tearful dark eyes, barely visible from the boat.

She mouthed, "Go." Then, her body relented against the officers and the fight within her ceased.

The boat jolted toward the sea and Nicholas turned to see Alius paddling as hard as he could. Nicholas spun once more to see the officers drag Lula out of the water, across the coarse wet sand of the shore. She no longer kicked or screamed, only watched with concerned eyes to make sure they escaped. Nicolas and Alius—she didn't care about herself. She'd always been more concerned for them.

As the small boat drifted further from the dock, the rain continued to pour. Nicholas's body collapsed from exhaustion. He had failed her. They would take her back to that horrible man, to live out the rest of her life at his commands. Should he go back? Would he be captured? He couldn't think straight.

"Um, Nicholas?" Alius shouted. "I know this isn't the best time . . ."

Nicholas glanced up to see a wave, five or six feet high, rolling toward them as lightning flashed overhead. He gripped the sides of the boat just as the wave broke, flooding the canoe. The vessel swayed back and forth as if it would flip, but thankfully righted itself before it did. Nicholas exhaled in relief.

"That was close," Alius shouted.

The storm continued to worsen, and the shadow of an even taller wave blocked the light of the distant moon overhead. A powerful wall of seawater hovered, as the whitecap broke and threatened their escape.

They paddled once again, a weak attempt at keeping control of the battered canoe. As the intensity of the wave rushed the boat, they overturned and Nicholas found himself caught underneath. Salty water filled his mouth as he fought against the instinct to swallow.

Again, a powerful wave crashed above him, flipping the

boat back around, and he kicked to the surface, reaching for the side before it drifted further from his grasp. His arms and legs were limp, exhausted from the struggle. Although it had been only minutes, it felt like hours before he managed to climb back into the boat. Nicholas sat up, searching the dark water for his friend.

"Al! Where are you?"

Silence.

"Al! Please! I'm right here, Buddy. I'll help you. Tell me where you are!" Tears filled his eyes and his heart pounded against his chest. "I'm here, Al!"

Silence.

Nicholas screamed with everything he had. "Al!" His voice hoarse with emotion, he gripped his throat.

He could no longer see the lantern lights on the shoreline, nor hear anything other than the calming waves after the storm. He stood on the canoe for hours, shouting for his best friend. No paddles. No food. Nicholas was at the mercy of the sea, and he'd lost the only family he had left.

He fell to his knees and screamed—his arms wrapping around his body as if he could hold himself together. Water rippled around him, taunting him. The boat continued to drift atop surging waves, then drop as they passed underneath.

Nicholas curled into a ball in the middle of the boat, gasping around painful sobs. His vision blurred and all at once, he threw himself over the boat, retching from nausea.

They were the only family he'd ever known and he swore he would protect them.

He had failed.

Part

Two

9

NICHOLAS

*N*ausea rolled through Nicholas with every sway of the boat. Curled on his side, he blinked against the brutal sun and licked across dry, split lips. He pushed up on one shaky elbow, but fell back against the rough wood of the paddle boat, weak and exhausted.

At first, his mind faltered as if it protected him from the memory—blocking every devastating detail from the night before. Or was it two days before? How long could he survive at sea with no food or water?

He placed a hand on the right side of his face, hot and painful from the sun overhead. Wincing, he jerked his palm away from the raw, blistered skin. At once, the smell of fish and seaweed assaulted his nose. He leaned over the side of the boat to vomit, but only managed to dry-heave as cramps seized his belly. Salt coated his throat, and his head pounded.

Ironic the things that spark a memory, he thought. A touch, the scent of honey and wildflowers in the summer, a melody . . .

On this day, the day Nicholas was sure his short life would end, his mind drifted back five years ago during an agonizing bout of food poisoning. He sat on the edge of the small bed, gently rocking and clutching his belly in pain, while Berta held the bucket in front of him.

The memory didn't resurface from his suffering, but the loneliness that overwhelmed him. Berta was not there with a cold cloth to wipe the sweat from his brow. Lula's soothing touch wasn't grazing across his back. He had no one. The priest was wrong, Nicholas thought. He didn't have a purpose. He was nothing.

Even his parents knew it.

Lula being captured and Alius's death weighed heavily on his heart, and the ache traveled up his chest and throat at the memory of the loss. "I deserve to die at sea," he whispered. A lonely and painful demise for a selfish boy like himself. He leaned back against the wooden flats, relaxing his head awkwardly on the bench across the middle.

When he closed his eyes, he didn't pray for himself. He asked God to watch over Lula and for Alius to rest in peace, away from the cruelty of the world. He spoke the names of the priests who were selfless and kind. For Berta, who watched over him when no one else would, and the other children at the orphanage with little hope of a future.

For Tomek, the sad soul on the train, to find his family and reunite—forgetting his painful past and forgiving himself. For Mr. Brunon to find happiness in something other than the torture of others. Lastly, he prayed for the family he never knew, hoping wherever they were—they knew love like he had shared with Lula and Alius.

SCRAPING, LOUD AND ROUGH, VIBRATED UNDERNEATH THE boat. Nicholas's eyelids fluttered, but he lacked the strength to open them.

"What's the story, Benson?" A booming voice with a thick Irish accent called out.

"Blow-in. He looks dead," Benson replied. He swept his hand through his shaggy brown hair and furrowed his brow at the sight before him.

The boat scraped against something hard once again and then pulled to the flat surface of sand. A calloused hand gripped Nicholas's chin and jerked his face toward the sun. Nicholas coughed, as if his lungs fought to expel the remaining seawater.

"Call the guards, let them handle the lad. Phillip will be back from the service soon and he'll expect us to be ready to leave. Plus, we need to get you home—or Staci will have your head."

"I hear ya. Doesn't look so good, George. Think the lad will make it?"

"Will he drink?" George asked. George, broad and tall, shuffled toward the boat, breathing heavily.

Cold metal hit Nicholas's lips as fresh water trickled into his mouth. His attempt to swallow ended in gagging, a reflex he couldn't control.

"Just a bit, now. There you are," Benson whispered.

Nicholas once again fought to blink, but the sunlight burned his sensitive eyes.

"Can't leave the lad, George. Not by his lonesome."

George stood, blocking the sun with one hand while taking in the local scene at the dock. "Patty! Patty, dear! Can you be of service to an old friend?"

"Old friend? You tried to slaughter my pig!" Patty shouted, her red hair sticking up in all directions.

"Well, it was plenty time. Feed my home for a month, he would!"

"He's a pet, you imbecile! Don't you touch him."

George rolled his eyes and attempted to change the

subject. "Young lad here needs a bit of help. We've sent for the guard, but it might be awhile since the service is today. They're all tied up and we hate to leave him by his lonesome."

Patty stretched her neck to peer inside the boat. "Not sure that one will make it. Better watch George, Benson. He'll try to feed him to his family."

"It's a boy, Patty! Not a bloody pig!" George shouted.

"Makes no difference to you, I'm sure!" Patty planted her fists on her hips and glared—every word full of fiery attitude.

George rolled his eyes and pointed toward Benson. "Get back to the dock. We're an Irish mile from home and we're leaving this bloody country behind."

Nicholas tried to speak up, but the effort was more than he could bear. He attempted to raise his head, but he fell limp against the boat. He could hear the men nearby, shuffling about the shoreline as if he wasn't stranded alone—dying. Nicholas felt himself drifting, blackness closing in, convincing him to let go of his consciousness. He had no idea how much time had gone by.

Again, he stirred when an authoritative voice of a man demanded attention.

"You sent for us?" Two men, dressed in dark suits, sat on horses, hovering over the Irish fisherman with a bored expression.

"Ah, yes. We discovered this young lad washed up on shore. Doesn't look so good, if you ask me."

One of the policemen swung his leg over the back of his horse and jumped to the ground, while the other refrained from budging. He peeked inside the canoe and shrugged.

"I'll pay a visit to the orphanage—see if there's room."

"He need a doctor?" Benson asked.

"Who will pay for it? You?" The guard asked with raised brows.

Benson stepped back, sheepishly.

"No room at the orphanage," a thick German accent rang out. "I can tell you that, now."

Every head swung toward the bank, where an older, dark-skinned gentleman in a black suit stood waiting.

"Sorry?" The policeman called out.

"The orphanage. No room," he grunted. "Heard 'em talking about it earlier. Better off finding a decent family to help."

The guard cleared his throat. "Are you volunteering?"

A light-hearted chuckle erupted from the man as he picked up the satchel beside him. "Got no use for a child."

The guard narrowed his eyes. "Then he can stay here."

"Here?" Patty called out. "All alone?"

"So, you will take him?"

"Me? My husband is traveling dear, Sir. Do you know what David would do if he came home to a strange child in the house? Would you allow your wife to accept another without consent?"

The guard tilted his head back and exhaled. "We don't have time for this. Either the orphanage or the street. Those are his options." The guard turned his back on Nicholas, who lay barely conscious in the narrow boat. The officers rode into town, ignoring the shocked expressions staring after them.

"Shame it is. Poor lad," mumbled George. He glanced up, as if remembering why he was there to begin with. "Ready there, Phillip?"

Phillip nodded, while staring at the child with something that looked like regret. "Best be moving. Home is calling."

George and Benson shuffled toward the dock to board their boat. Benson turned repeatedly toward Nicholas with sad eyes, as if he wished he could do something for the boy.

A loud sigh escaped the man they referred to as Phillip as he remained, satchel in hand. He took small steps, as if somewhat curious. He gazed into the side of the canoe, and tilted his head deep in thought.

"Good workin' age he is. Might be a big help to someone, wouldn't you say, Phillip?" Patty grinned.

"I know what you're doing, Patty."

"I'm not sure what you mean."

"Got no use for another mouth to feed. Connie might not appreciate it." Phillip walked away without another word.

Nicholas didn't know how long he had laid there, but the heat of the sun faded into the cool of night. He stirred at the feeling of another's presence, desperate for help but also fearful of not being able to defend himself. Nicholas fought against the pounding in his head to squint at the face above him. An old man, with skin as black as the night sky, stared down at him with the largest, warmest brown eyes he'd ever seen. The dark chocolate of his gaze reminded him of Lula and his chest tightened from the memory.

"One night, so you don't die out here all alone. Come now, Son. Let's get you home."

The elderly man lifted Nicholas and supported him while he stumbled from the canoe. Shaky hands pulled him over the back of a horse. He laid on his belly, his head hanging off one side as the clomp of hooves lulled him into darkness.

NICHOLAS WOKE WARM AND COZY. HE KNEW HE'D DIED— there was no other explanation. Although heavy, his eyelids flickered in the dimly lit room, fighting to absorb his surroundings. Would he meet the angels Father Gorski spoke of?

He jolted as a drop of cold water hit his forehead and made a path down his temple. He opened his eyes and a blurry image of dark wooden planks hovered over him.

Again, a drop of water fell from the ceiling and hit him in the face, as if attempting to wake him. Surely this wasn't heaven. He couldn't imagine God having trouble with leaky roofs.

He turned his head as reality set in. It was a small space, but open with the lack of furniture or belongings. The ceiling sat low and the bed felt more like a cot—as Nicholas's feet hung off the end. The strong smell of fish and herbs hovered and a combination of hunger pangs and nausea settled within the pit of his stomach.

A small fire in the hearth illuminated the dark cabin and the low hum in his ears dulled, replaced by the crooning of a soulful voice. A tall, somewhat lanky man sat hunched in front of the flames, gently rocking as he sang an unfamiliar tune.

He thought of Berta, belting loudly with her high-pitched voice—such a contrast to the old man sitting before him. Nicholas closed his eyes as the music seeped into his soul. It relaxed him. Comforted him. He turned on his side toward the fire and the bed creaked, halting the smooth melody.

"You're awake." The man's deep voice called out.

Nicholas whispered, "Yes, Sir."

They sat in silence for several minutes before the old man spoke up once again. "Made a liar of me, you did."

"Sorry?" Nicholas asked, confused.

"Said you could stay one night. It's been three."

Three nights? Had it really been that long? The man still hadn't turned toward him. Was he angry? Nicholas pushed up on his elbows and stretched his neck from side to side.

"Got some water in you. Only thing that saved you."

"Thank you. I'll be out of your way. I didn't mean to impose." Nicholas slowly sat up, but dizziness kept him from moving further.

"Middle of the night, Son. You can leave tomorrow." The

man slid a bowl halfway across the floor toward Nicholas, then turned and continued singing.

Nicholas eased from the bed, his muscles cold and stiff. He had on the same clothes that he'd worn when he left Father Gorski's, minus his boots, except the pants hung on his hips slightly more than before. His knees shook, and the skin of his hands dry and tight from dehydration as he clenched his fists.

Kneeling on the floor beside the bowl, Nicholas's hand trembled as he balanced the spoon mid-air. The soup sloshed until a frail, wrinkled hand reached forward and steadied his arm.

"Thank you," Nicholas whispered. He leaned in, slurping the hot broth, then sat back on his heels and sighed.

"Good?"

"Very," Nicholas replied.

The old man chuckled. "Easy there. Start slow."

The more he managed to swallow, the better he felt. The hot liquid soothed the dryness and he breathed a sigh of relief at the comfort.

"Where am I?" Nicholas asked.

"Brusberg."

"Poland?" Nicholas asked with a furrowed brow.

"Germany."

Nicholas's spoon clanged against the ceramic bowl and his eyes widened. "Germany? But . . . But that's far from Poland."

"Few hours by sea. Few days by foot. Depends on how you look at it. Is that where you're from?"

"Yes. I grew up in an orphanage in Torek. My friend, Lula, is in Dalbeca. I have to get back to her."

"I think you best be worried about getting your strength right now, Son. The rest will come in due time."

Nicholas nodded, knowing he was right. He couldn't

rescue Lula in his current state, but he would go back for her. He'd promised. Glancing down at the watery-thin broth, he wondered if his word meant anything at all. He told Lula and Alius he would watch over them. Nicholas said things would be different for them when they left the orphanage—better.

His promises meant nothing.

Sitting in front of the weak flames, burning with as much energy as he felt, Nicholas made one final promise to himself. A vow to pick himself up and follow through with this journey they began together.

"I'm Nicholas. Nicholas Dalbeck."

"Glad to meet you, Nicholas. I'm Eulas. Eulas Klaus."

10

NICHOLAS

*T*he sun peeked over rows of apple trees through the window, and the bright rays of orange and yellow swept across Nicholas's face from his straw padding on the floor. Eulas would wake soon and for the first time, Nicholas was determined to be out the door before the old man's feet hit the floor.

It had been five days since Nicholas woke to meet the German farmer who saved his life. Five days of healing, physically and emotionally. He'd watched Eulas on the farm, day after day, tending to the lush fields and small collection of animals in the barn. But today, he would do the work. His depleted strength regained, he would show his appreciation by helping the kind soul who refused to let him die alone on the shore.

Nicholas wasn't entirely sure he was welcome, but Eulas had yet to broach the subject. There was no comfortable conversation in the evening, no laughter or entertaining tales of years gone by. Every night, after a quiet dinner, Eulas laid on the small cot of a bed and Nicholas on the floor until they drifted off to sleep. Once, Nicholas swore he felt the brush of the old man's hand on his forehead, as if checking for a fever, but surely he dreamt it.

The sad truth was Nicholas had nowhere to go. No family or friends. The orphanage was over capacity. If he could prove himself to Eulas, maybe he would let him stay. At least long enough to forge a plan to rescue Lula.

He sat up, slipping into old worn clothes, the only set he owned, and eased the door open just enough to slip through. Even with the cover of the porch, sunlight assaulted his eyes, encouraging him to absorb the brilliance of the morning sky.

He loved the view from the cabin. Sometimes in the evening he would sit in one of the weathered rocking chairs, the creaking of the old wood soothing him like a lullaby. A summer breeze, if only for a moment, would blow through the small farm as the sunset illuminated the land in a dim glow of burning embers. He'd close his eyes and pretend Lula and Alius were by his side, and everything was right with the world. Their loss was almost unbearable at times. The look of terror in Lula's gaze and panicked shouts from Alius in his final moments haunted Nicholas every night as he closed his eyes.

Nicholas picked up the small basket with a linen towel folded in the bottom. He'd seen Eulas collect eggs for several days and he was confident he could handle it. The small barn sat behind the cottage, and housed a tidy chicken coup with bales of hay and farm equipment. An overweight pig and irritable mule grunted and snorted as he walked by, as if annoyed by his presence.

Small nesting boxes on the right were attached to the barn wall with feathers and straw hanging from the slight openings. Most of the huhns pecked around the ground, waiting for their handful of corn they knew would soon come. All but one.

The biggest, ugliest chicken he'd ever seen, stretched her

neck toward him—daring him to make a move. Fuzzy brown feathers framed a speckled face with one black eye, the other scarred and white. Nicholas swore every animal in the barn froze to witness the stand-off, anxious for the deranged huhn to take down the strange boy.

He slipped by the peering black eye and gathered the eggs within reach. While sneaking by the coup to make a quiet exit—he saw the brown shells of eggs hidden under the crazy chicken.

Eulas would expect him to be thorough.

Nicholas reached forward, his hand shaking as the black eye widened.

As soon as he made contact with the egg, a horrific and alarming cackle echoed inside the barn. There was no time to react. No time to regret his actions. A brown shroud of feathers covered his face as sharp talons clung to his scalp. Nicholas blindly bolted from the barn, screaming as the sharp peck of a beak collided against his skull. His life flashed before his eyes and shame consumed him at the thought of being taken down by a huhn.

Nicholas ran chaotically outside, until the hard thump of a fence post stopped him in his tracks, knocking him backwards to the ground. A sweet, high-pitched voice cooed over him as the talons softly released and sunlight blinded him.

A tall girl with tan skin, long, curly brown hair and hazel eyes clutched the huhn to her chest and stroked the unruly feathers down the chicken's back. The black eye of the hen continued to glare, as if daring him to move. He wouldn't.

"What are you doing to this poor animal?" The girl asked, horrified.

"Me? It tried to claw my eyes out! That chicken is insane!"

"Nonsense. You only frightened her. Here you go. I'll take you back to rest. I know you have to be terrified." The girl shuffled back to the barn, singing softly to the deranged hen.

"Nicholas?"

Nicholas jerked his head toward the fence post where Eulas stood, his brows pulled low in confusion. Nicholas scampered to his feet quickly, ashamed he couldn't finish one chore.

"I'm sorry, Sir. I wanted to gather the eggs, but I'm afraid I don't know how to handle your chickens."

"Handle my chickens?" Eulas's gaze traveled toward the barn and his eyes widened at the realization. "You tried to handle Heidi?"

"Heidi? Well, is uh, is that the huhn?" Nicholas asked.

Eulas nodded, trying not to smile.

"There were eggs, Mr. Klaus. I only wanted to collect them all."

"Son, Heidi hasn't laid eggs in three months. As chickens age, they stop producing."

"But the eggs..." Nicholas tried to explain.

"Those were her last lay and she's been mighty protective of them. I didn't have the heart to take them from her."

"So you've just left them?"

"Of course. She'd claw my eyes out." Eulas chuckled and turned toward the house. Halfway there, he turned and peered over at Nicholas. "You don't want one of those eggs to break, Son. It'll stink to high heaven."

Then he was gone.

Nicholas collapsed on the ground, attempting to catch his breath and slow his pounding heart. A shadow broke through the sunlight above as disapproving eyes judged him.

"Thanks for your help," Nicholas called out. He pushed up on his elbows, then stood to face his rescuer.

"You really shouldn't handle them if you don't know what you're doing. You stressed her out."

"She stressed me out," he mumbled.

"What was that?"

"I said you're absolutely right," Nicholas corrected.

The girl stood a bit straighter and tilted her chin up at his admission. "I'm Minna." She swept her palm down the front of her white skirt, then held her hand out to shake.

Nicholas grinned and clutched her hand. "I'm Nicholas."

The young girl's face changed—softened under Nicholas's intense blue eyes. She cleared her throat and pulled her hand away, as if uncomfortable. "The orphanage sends someone over every now and then to help keep things up. Mr. Klaus's eggs and potatoes have fed us for years, so this is our way of giving back."

"You're from the orphanage?"

Minna nodded, then lowered her head in shame.

Guilt consumed Nicholas. He knew this feeling all too well. "I grew up in an orphanage in Torek."

Minna glanced up, surprised. "You did? How did you get here?"

"It's, well it's a long story."

Minna nodded, but didn't push for more.

Her long narrow nose and high cheekbones reminded him of the tales of fairies Berta used to read at bedtime. She slouched as if self-conscious, then her thin lips pulled back in a fake smile as if to ease the awkwardness.

"I need to feed the chickens, so I guess I should go," he mumbled.

She nodded once again, but didn't move. She kicked a rock with the toe of her brown boot then met his eyes. "I can ask Ms. Willa if I can help more often on the farm, if you want. Maybe show you a few things. She'll be happy to hear the land has a farmhand." Her lack of self-esteem kept her from keeping eye contact. She turned, taking in the land around her. "It will be time for harvesting soon, and you can't do that by yourself."

"Harvesting?"

Her eyes widened in shock. "The potatoes. You really don't know anything do you?"

Nicholas chuckled. "I guess not."

"Thank heavens I'm here."

Nicholas was taken aback by her honesty. He didn't know how to respond to this feisty, yet self-conscious girl before him. He'd never met anyone like her.

"Does that mean you're going to help me?"

"Sure. But you'll owe me." Minna placed her hands on her hips and tilted her chin up."

"Owe you? I don't have anything."

She grinned, and Nicholas felt quite nervous all of a sudden.

"I'll think of something."

MINNA HURRIED TOWARD THE ORPHANAGE, AND NICHOLAS hesitantly turned toward the barn. He imagined this was how men felt when going into battle, wondering if they'd walk away unscathed.

Heidi perched on her rotting eggs, refusing to leave the last of her youthful years behind. She eyed his every move, and clucked twice when she didn't like his proximity to her nest. After spreading the corn for the huhns, Nicholas located the bucket of grain for the hog—who also wasn't happy about his presence.

The large pig, who Eulas referred to as Franz, laid in the shaded corner of the pen, snorting like a bull preparing to charge. The pen was nothing more than two rows of wooden planks, and Nicholas knew Franz could easily escape if he chose. He tip-toed inside the small fence, determined to make it quick. As soon as he dumped the grain for Franz, a terrifying squeal rang out and the heavy clomp of hooves barrelled in his direction.

Nicholas spun toward the massive charging pig, snorting and screeching for all to hear. He fumbled back toward the edge of the pen, away from the threatening beast, in time for Baret, the crotchety mule, to rear up his hind legs and kick him in the back.

Nicholas flew forward from the impact and landed face first in Franz's water trough. He stumbled to his feet, soaked. His lower back ached from Baret's strike and he turned, glaring at the large gray mule with the wiry mane. He almost looked amused.

Nicholas stomped out of the pen, water sloshing from his trousers and the smell of Franz filling his nose. He took deep breaths to calm the anger within. Why did he think he could do this?

Failure. That's all he knew.

He stomped to the front porch where Eulas sat in a rocker, watching him with hawk-like eyes. Nicholas sat down without a word, staring out over the orchard.

"They know you're scared, Son." Eulas rocked back and forth, humming an unfamiliar tune.

"They?" Nicholas asked.

"The animals. They can smell it."

Nicholas shook his head, more annoyed than he ever remembered feeling. "All I can smell is Franz."

Eulas chuckled. "You tried. That's all I can ask."

"Is that enough, though? I feel like I've been trying my whole life and it hasn't gotten me anywhere."

"It got you here. Exactly where you're supposed to be on this day—at this hour. The rest will come."

A soulful hum filled the summer air and Nicholas watched as Eulas closed his eyes, absorbing the warmth of the day—confident in a greater plan Nicholas had yet to understand. The dark lines around his eyes were evidence of more wisdom than Nicholas could ever imagine at his young age.

"You believe that? You believe there's a point to all of this?" Nicholas asked.

Eulas smiled. "I do."

11

NICHOLAS

*T*he end of summer drew near, and Eulas worked Nicholas tirelessly to prepare for the potato harvest. Baret kicked and whined from his enclosed fence, as if anxious to be put to use. Nicholas figured that was all anyone could ever hope for in this life—to be of use. To have purpose.

Although, he began to wonder if Baret was only there to make Nicholas's life difficult. From the bruises down his back, it crossed his mind. The mule had clearly made his feelings known.

When Eulas freed Baret from the confines of his pen, the mule—obedient and responsive—followed Eulas toward the fields and stood in front of the plow, waiting patiently. Nicholas narrowed his eyes at the stubborn beast. He would never cooperate with anyone like he did with Mr. Klaus.

When Baret began to turn the soil, Nicholas's eyes widened at the potatoes rolling to the surface. They spent the entire afternoon plowing up the rich lot of vegetables. Mr. Klaus decided to turn in for the night, exhausted, and instructed Nicholas to begin harvesting the following morning.

Minna showed bright and early the next day, demonstrating the proper way to sack potatoes. She was smart, hard-working, and thrived in the rich soil of farmland. If anyone was made for this life, it was her. Nothing pulled the brilliant smile of joy from her pretty face like filthy hands and the warmth of summer sun.

Eulas stayed in bed for most of that day, and Nicholas knew the plowing had been hard on him. He didn't bring it up for fear of being disrespectful.

Minna kneeled, the cream skirt forgotten, and started pulling up the vegetables, throwing them in burlap sacks.

She glanced over her shoulder and squawked, "What are you waiting for, Nicholas? An invite?"

Nicholas jumped from his daze and dove into the dark soil alongside her. It thrilled him to be a part of something so productive—so meaningful. Hundreds and hundreds of potatoes hovered on the surface, waiting to be gathered.

After an hour of harvesting, it wasn't as thrilling. His back ached and knees throbbed from hunching forward on the ground. The image of Eulas working the farm year after year tormented him. How did he manage it on his own?

The timid voice of Minna broke through his thoughts as they continued working side by side in the potato fields. "Nicholas, tell me how you came to Mr. Klaus's farm. I've been curious."

Nicholas cleared his throat. "I thought I had a purpose, I guess. My dream was to share Christmas with the world and I failed. Lost my two best friends and almost died at sea. That's when I woke up here. It's embarrassing, really. Do you think less of me?"

"Of course not!" she exclaimed. Minna's larger than average eyes widened in shock at what he'd been through.

"That's just awful. Didn't they teach you about Christmas in Torek?"

"Father Krol taught us the lesson behind it, yes. I want to feel Christmas. Know what I mean?"

Minna smiled and started to nod, but it quickly transformed into a confused expression—her eyes narrowed and she pursed her lips as she shook her head. "No, not really."

Nicholas chuckled. "No matter anyway. I'm just a foolish boy with absurd dreams. We all have to grow up eventually, right?" Nicholas continued scooping the potatoes into his sack, as if he hadn't come to the heartbreaking realization at that very moment.

A sad smile broke across her face as she watched him continue his work. "Some of us more quickly than others, I suppose."

HARVESTING WEEK WASN'T FOR THE FAINT OF HEART. BLOOD, sweat and tears went into every sack of potatoes that year, and Eulas beamed with pride at the reaping. He'd admitted to Nicholas one evening that he rarely gathered the entire yield, because of his lack of physical strength.

Minna arrived at the end of the week to load several sacks of potatoes for the orphanage. Eulas instructed him to store some for the winter, and to sell the rest at market to replenish his dwindling funds. Nicholas laid down every night, on his straw filled pallet and slept with the comforting knowledge he had made a difference in someone's life—for once.

A couple of weeks after harvest, Nicholas laid awake in the darkness, his mind in a different time and place. It was in these quiet, solitary moments when he missed Lula and Alius the most. The companionship and conversation—the only family he'd ever known.

"How am I supposed to sleep with you thinking so loud?" Eulas asked, irritated.

Nicholas chuckled. "I didn't realize you could think at different volumes."

"Me either, til you moved in," he mumbled. "Something on your mind?"

"No, Sir. Well, yes. But, no, nevermind." Nicholas closed his eyes at his ridiculousness.

"Which is it?" Eulas asked.

"Yes, Sir. There's something on my mind." He threw his arm over his face, embarrassed, although no one could see him in the darkness of the cottage.

"I don't have all night. Sleep is due for an old man like myself."

Nicholas took a deep breath and exhaled slowly. He'd told himself these words over and over, but admitting them to someone else sent a fresh wave of pain through his chest. Like a knife to a barely healed wound.

"I failed my friends—the only family I have. What kind of person puts their best friends in danger over foolish dreams of Christmas?"

Silence filled the cottage, thick with anger and regret from Nicholas.

Eulas didn't respond immediately, as if pondering the boy's words. He cleared his throat and mumbled, "What's this about Christmas?"

"Christmas?" Nicholas asked. He fully expected to be chastised over the selfishness of putting his friends in danger, and Eulas' question surprised him. "I, well, I've always been drawn to the holiday, Sir. Father Krol taught us all about it at the orphanage, but something was missing. I don't feel as though I fully grasp it, you know? We ran away to find our family in hopes of finding the true meaning of it all."

"The priest taught you the history of Christmas?"

"He did. I can't help but feel as though there is more. Like God wants us to breathe Christmas—not just celebrate it. I know that sounds foolish."

"Only proud fools are foolish, Son. You are no fool. The birth of Christ is one of the most important events in our history, along with His death and resurrection. Do you understand that?"

"Oh, yes Sir. I do. But shouldn't you feel something? I keep waiting for a thrilling explosion inside every year when Christmas arrives. I want to experience the joy of feasting with family and singing carols. . ."

"So, you've learned about it, but haven't experienced it."

Nicholas's eyes widened at his understanding. "Exactly!"

"Alright. We'll work on that. One step at a time, though. An old man can only handle so much, you know. What is this about your friends?"

Tears filled his eyes in the darkness and Nicholas blinked, thankful Mr. Klaus couldn't witness his moment of weakness. "We escaped Dalbeca in a boat. The police caught up with us and took Lula. Then, the storm flipped our canoe and I lost Alius in the waves. My best friend is gone —drowned."

Nicholas sniffled at the memory of that night. "He almost died at sea as a child, trying to save his brother. I guess the ocean never gave up. Horrible thing for someone so kind."

"That's, well, that is unfortunate, Nicholas. I'm sorry for your loss. What about the girl? Lula?"

"Her father is a horrible man and I have to get her away from him. How am I supposed to do that? I'm in Germany and she's in Poland. If I could just talk to Lula—tell her I won't give up."

"Have you thought of writing to her? Surely you know someone who would get the letter to Lula. Think, Son. You're more clever than you realize."

Nicholas turned over his words, considering every possible option. He didn't know Father Gorski's address, but he could send it to St. Marys. He had faith the priests would help him. "I believe I do."

"That a boy. Send the girl a letter. Be smart about it. You need to know her situation before you barrel into town on a rescue mission. If you get yourself killed, what would she do then?"

Nicholas nodded, feeling proactive for the first time since washing ashore in Brusberg. Eulas was right. This time he would be smart about it.

"First thing in the morning, I'm going to write to her. Thank you, Sir. That is brilliant!"

"You'll be taking potatoes to the market tomorrow. You can drop your letter off along the way. Get some sleep. I can't fix all of your problems in one night."

"Yes, Sir."

Nicholas laid on the floor with his hands behind his head, staring up at the ceiling. In the black of night, he could barely make out the small crack in the wood—the tiniest gleam of moonlight begging to be noticed. He thought of everything he would say to Lula.

How would she feel after hearing about Alius's death? Would she still want to marry him? Please God, don't let her hate me, he prayed. He could bring her back to Germany and she could help on the farm. Lula and Minna could become friends.

"Nicholas?" Eulas asked.

"Yes, Sir?"

"Is she pretty?" A smidge of humor filled Eulas's voice.

"The prettiest."

"Oh dear."
"Yes, Sir."

Dear Lula,

I can only pray you receive this letter. I think of you every day, hoping you are safe and well. Little else occupies my thoughts. I need to tell you, Alius is gone. Our sweet, funny, devoted friend was lost at sea and I'm completely heartbroken. Please forgive me for putting you in this situation and for not protecting Alius. It will haunt me for the rest of my life.

I will come back for you, I promise. I am safe, with an older man by the name of Eulas Klaus in Germany. I've learned to farm potatoes, tend the orchards and care for the animals—although they hate me. I wish you were here. Maybe one day, we can have a farm together.

Please let me know, in some way, that you are safe. I'm coming back for you, sweet Lula.

Yours truly,
Nicholas

1 2

LULA

$\mathcal{L}$ula lowered her head as she ambled down the uneven cobblestone street in Dalbeca. The heat of the sun beat down on the back of her neck as it always did when walking through town. Mr. Brunon's trips became fewer and fewer now that he had Lula to do his bidding.

The locals didn't complain. They would much rather deal with her than the crotchety old man. Plus, the break away from the stuffy house did wonders for her mood—a reminder that life still existed. Sometimes she wondered if there would be a life for her at all, full of hope and love. With Nicholas gone, she'd lost faith in a happily ever after for herself.

She could hear it—the second set of footsteps, loud and clumsy, matching her own. The shadow crept closer, but she didn't acknowledge the presence of another. She wouldn't do anything to bring attention to herself and have word travel back to Mr. Brunon.

She knew better.

Her eyes focused on the stone laid out before her feet, like always, never meeting the sympathetic eyes of the residents of the town. A woman had stopped her weeks before, asking if she could bandage the large gash above her brow. Lula had paid dearly for that act of kindness when she arrived home with the cut covered. He wanted her to see the nasty wound, a reminder of what would happen when she didn't comply. She'd learned it was better to ignore the pleasantries and generosity of her neighbors. They didn't understand the effect their attention had on her life.

A particularly red cobblestone—dark with a black spot in the right upper corner—drifted underneath her feet and she knew the general store would be on her left in fifty more steps. Just like she knew when her left foot dipped into an uneven spot by the white fence, the bakery would be on her right.

She could still hear the footsteps behind her. A small alleyway beside the general store sat empty, all except a day's worth of trash and a couple of hungry felines. It smelled of rotten fruit and wet hair, and Lula breathed through her mouth so she wouldn't gag. No one would wander into the alley after them, so she knew it was safe.

When she reached the darkest, farthest side of the alley from the street, she spun toward her stalker with narrowed eyes and clenched fists. "Why are you following me?"

"I need to talk to you. It's important."

"You know what he will do to me, Alius. I can't be seen with you!"

Alius's face fell and his nostrils flared as if he'd cry. "There's a letter."

Lula leaned forward, shaking her head. "A letter? From who?"

"Nicholas." Alius's face softened.

She stepped back, hitting the rough brick of the wall of the building as if she'd collapse. "He's alive? You're saying he's alive?"

"This arrived at St. Mary's, then sent to Father Gorski. He asked me to sneak it to you when I caught you alone."

Lula's eyes drifted across the wrinkled envelope in his palm, shaking and sweaty. Her delicate hand reached forward and pulled the letter from his grip—never taking her gaze from the parcel. They'd cried and prayed over Nicholas for weeks. She truly thought he'd died at sea.

She slid down the brick wall, afraid her legs would give way when reading his words. Her fingers tore through the soft, thin paper and scanned the handwriting she never thought she would see again.

He was alive.

Nicholas had survived against all odds. Hot tears ran down her cheeks as the meaning of his written words penetrated the fog of emotions. He was coming back for her. Her eyes drifted from the parchment to Alius, who stood shuffling from one foot to another, impatiently.

"Well? What's it say, Lu? Don't leave me frettin'."

She slid the paper across the ground toward his feet, and Alius sat, somewhat awkwardly, in front of her. As he took in every word, his chin quivered and his fingers tightened, crinkling the edges of the letter.

"I tried to get back to the boat that night, Lu. You have to believe me. It was so dark and the waves were too strong."

"I know, Alius. I believe you," she whispered. "I'm just thankful Father Gorski found you before it was too late."

"Do you think Nicholas will really come back? He sounds happy. Don't ya think?"

Lula nodded and began to cry. She buried her head in her hands, releasing the pent up sadness she'd harbored for weeks. More than any thirteen-year-old girl should have to endure.

Alius scooted across the ground, offering comfort in their few minutes of isolation. "Awe, Lu. I'm sorry. I didn't mean to make you cry." He patted her, rather roughly, on the back, as if he wasn't quite sure what to do with a weeping girl.

"It's not your fault, Al. It's just, well, I miss him so much."

"He's alive, Lula. It won't be long before he comes back and we can all leave together, just as we planned." Alius's eyes brightened with the thought of a reunion.

The bitter truth struck Lula harder than any blow she'd taken the past few weeks. Nicholas could never return. If he did, they would lock him up and his life would be over. The guards blamed her entire escape on Nicholas that night and it was the only reason Alius walked free.

She blinked, her eyelids weighed down by the fatigue of sleepless nights. No—she would never see Nicholas again. She had to make sure of it.

"Alius, we can't let him come back. You know what they'll do."

Alius shook his head, disagreeing before the words left her lips. "We'll be smarter. Quicker this time," he promised.

Lula stopped him by placing her hand on his. "I'm sorry. I won't risk his life or his future. We both know Nicholas has a purpose far greater than we understand. Don't you want him to find out what that is?"

Alius's shoulders slumped. "Of course. But I miss my friend, Lu. My brother."

"Do you remember what Father Gorski told Nicholas? There's a time for everything. He is out there finding himself and we need to let him."

Lula gripped Alius's hand, comforting her friend the only way she knew how. It was hard—she mourned Nicholas every day.

"We have to let him go." Her whispered words were filled with heartache and despair. At least she knew he was alive and well.

That would have to be enough.

"How are we supposed to do that? You know he won't give up on you, Lula. He promised. Look, it says right here in the letter." Alius held up the small piece of paper as if she'd forgotten it existed. "Plus, you know he'll come back when he finds out I survived."

"I'm going to send one back, Alius. I'll tell him I've decided to stay. He needs to believe I'm happy—I won't mention you." Lula's tearful gaze refused to meet Alius's.

"You're going to lie to him?"

Lula bit her bottom lip to keep it from quivering. "I'm going to lie."

His mouth fell open in shock. "You're not thinking straight, Lu. You can't do this to him. It will kill him."

"And if he comes back? What do you think they will do? He won't have a future, Alius. I won't let him risk his life for me. I'm sorry."

Alius looked down, unable to meet her eyes. "I understand you're protecting him, but it will break his heart."

Her eyes were filled with resolve—Lula had made up her mind. "He needs to stay where he is. Are you with me or not?"

Alius froze as if he didn't know what to do, then nodded. "I'm always with you."

My Dear Nicholas,

It does my heart good to hear from you. I'm so thankful you are safe. I'm sorry this is so brief, but there is little to be said. We've always clung to each other in the pit of loneliness of our youth. We didn't have anyone else. Now, things are different.

I have a home—a father. I'm settling quite well in Dalbeca and look forward to a happy and long life here. Hopefully I will marry and have children of my own one day. I need you to let go of our childish dreams of happily-ever-after and find your own path. One you can be content with. I will forever hold onto the memories we shared.

With love,
Lula Mae Dunivant

13

NICHOLAS

*B*right red drops of blood fell from Nicholas's lip, staining the purity of the new fallen snow. Ironically, some days he felt like a stain himself—tarnished and dirty. For the first time in his life, the magic of Christmas hadn't sparked the need it had before. For the first time, he thought only of the next chore. The next physically demanding task that would numb the heartache.

Nicholas felt broken.

Four months ago, he felt the loss of Alius and Lula all over again—and he hadn't gotten over it. After receiving Lula's letter, he crumpled it under his straw-filled mattress and stomped outside without a word. He didn't speak for days, and Eulas didn't push. He gave Nicholas his space and plenty to do on the farm to occupy his mind.

One day, Nicholas walked through the front door from cleaning the pig sty and caught Eulas sitting by the fire reading Lula's letter. Now Eulas would understand. He would know that no one wanted Nicholas. Would he cast him aside also? Nicholas fought the bubbling anger from rising to the surface.

Nicholas shuffled across the room, holding his hand out for the letter. His nose flared and eyes watered, but he stayed silent. Eulas's gaze studied the disheartened young man in front of him, then handed the letter over. Nicholas gripped the crumpled paper, froze from the confusion and pain it brought, then tossed it into the flames. He laid down on his thin pallet without a word and fell asleep before supper. Eulas allowed him a few more days of wallowing before approaching the subject.

"I want you to go to the orphanage starting tomorrow, attend school with the other children. You can sleep here, if you like, but you need interaction with kids your age, Son. It might help."

So that's how Nicholas ended up in that situation, bloody and ticked off. It felt as if the bully, Hans, knew every possible way to rile him—as if there was no other purpose in his miserable life.

The week before, Hans strolled up to Nicholas in the dining hall, demanding his portion of kasza. Nicholas stood eye to eye with Hans, refusing to relent. Hans smiled, snatched up the bowl of kasza from the small boy named Gavin and began eating it in front of everyone. Then he turned and walked away with the boy's food. Gavin teared up, unable to defend himself.

"Here ya go, Gavin," Nicholas mumbled as he slid his bowl toward the small boy. "You can have mine."

He had no patience for a bully.

That particular day, Hans accused Nicholas of trying to move in on his girl, Christine. A petite young girl with dark brown ringlets and black eyes. Minna said Christine didn't like Hans and wanted Nicholas's attention, and Hans knew it. He was apparently jealous.

So they fought, again. He could call Nicholas every name imaginable, laugh at his clothes, taunt him—he didn't care.

When Hans insulted Mr. Klaus, he lost it. Hans smirked as he called Nicholas a farmhand of an old black man who'd lived a meaningless life. Hans continued to poke and prod until Nicholas tackled him, and they rolled across the courtyard of the school with Minna yelling to hit Hans harder.

She was always in Nicholas's corner.

No matter. It gave Nicholas something to think about, other than all he'd lost the past few months. Nothing could be as painful. He didn't bother going into the cottage. The firewood inside dwindled night after night and he knew they'd need more from the barn.

The priest expected him back for Christmas Eve Mass, but Nicholas couldn't imagine returning. How quickly something so extraordinary dimmed. The light that once guided his purpose had faded into an emptiness inside.

Jerking the barn door open against the dense pile of snow, Nicholas trudged forward through the smell of hay and chicken manure, without sparing a glance at the clucking hens or squealing Franz. He placed one hand on the split log on top and froze, taking in the dried blood along his fist—the abrasions from hitting sharp rocks on the ground during his scuffle.

He didn't realize he was crying until tears dripped down his arm, creating a path through the layer of dirt on his forearm. Nicholas stared as if he couldn't comprehend the sight. He gripped the log tighter, but it only seemed to intensify the emotion welling within. He couldn't take it anymore. He felt . . . lost.

"Nicholas?" Eulas's deep voice echoed throughout the barn.

Silence.

"I'd like for you to finish up here. We have somewhere to be tonight."

Nicholas had enough respect for Eulas to obey without

question. "Yes, Sir." He felt the old man's presence behind him, hovering as if he wanted to say more. He didn't. Eulas turned away from the barn, giving Nicholas his space.

Nicholas closed his eyes and spoke aloud as if someone would answer. "I believed I had a purpose. That I could make a difference. I risked the lives of my friends and nearly got myself killed because I thought all of this would lead me to the spirit of Christmas—the meaning of something greater than I'd ever experienced. I'm nothing more today than I was at the orphanage. A nobody."

Nicholas wiped the tears from his face and stacked the rough, dry wood in his arms. After taking a deep breath, he shuffled out into the bitter cold, away from the shelter of the barn. His ears throbbed from the assault of the wind and his eyes burned. He hurried into the cottage just as the sun began to set over the mountainside.

A hearty rich aroma filled the small space of the cabin and his stomach growled at the sight of Christmas dinner on the small wooden table. Nicholas's gaze drifted to the side of the room at the small pine tree decorated with homemade tinsel. He melted at the sight of the small wooden bed beside the tree, taking the place of the hay mattress he'd grown accustomed to.

"Not much, but I did make it myself. Merry Christmas."

Nicholas didn't know what to say. He kneeled down, placing the dry logs beside the fire, then turned toward Eulas. "I, um, never had a Christmas gift before," Nicholas muttered. "I didn't get you anything."

"You've given me more than you know." Eulas turned, as if another thought occurred. "One more thing. Found this on the porch. I believe that pretty girl from the orphanage left it."

Nicholas pulled the loose brown wrapping, revealing a red and white knitted toboggan. He pulled the hat over his head and a grin replaced the emotionless expression he'd worn for weeks. Nicholas's heart, that had become as hard as stone, softened.

"Thank you. You and Minna have been so good to me."

"I've said it before. You're a good boy, Nicholas. Just had a bad run. After dinner, I'm gonna keep my promise. I'll show you what Christmas means to me."

NICHOLAS AND EULAS SAT AT THE UNSTEADY TABLE, THE LEGS shifting on the uneven floor from the weight of their elbows. They didn't pay any attention to that though. Eulas entertained Nicholas with stories of his childhood, the hardships and how his family came to Germany. He told him of his tradition of knipp sausage with red cabbage and how his mother taught him to make the best apple preserves in all of the land.

"After your parents died, has it always been just you?"

Eulas stared down at the plate, pushing his cabbage from one side to the other. "No. No it wasn't." Eulas cleared his throat, then exhaled. "I fell in love at an early age, much like yourself. I'll never forget the first time I saw her. Her ruffled white dress and red silk scarf tied around her head. When Alma agreed to marry me, I felt invincible. Nothing in the world could touch what we had. That is, until cholera spread throughout Germany. I was twenty-two when I lost her. Swore there would never be another. Not like her."

"I'm so sorry," Nicholas whispered.

Eulas nodded. "We wanted a big family. Lots of children." He met Nicholas's eyes and his expression brightened. "I've always dreamed of retelling the wonders of Magisfjell that my Pa taught us growing up."

"Magisfjell? What is that?"

"The Norwegians referred to it as the Magic Mountain. An island of thick ice covered in twenty feet of snow year round. Legend says it's the source of the aurora, and is lit by the mystical swirl of lights every night."

"You've never seen it then?"

"No. No, I haven't. I always hoped to, but it felt as if my work wasn't finished here. My brother went in search of it years ago. Father spoke of stone caves and fishing every morning before sunrise." Eulas chuckled. "He said the snow is dreadful, but you'll never find more beautiful land. Maybe we can go together one day. That would be something, wouldn't it?"

Nicholas never understood what it meant to have a real family. Someone to teach and guide you. Someone who never gave up on you. He could never imagine the strong connection that came with blood ties. At that moment, he realized he knew exactly what that meant. Eulas cared for him while sick, taught him about love, and never once treated him like an orphan. It didn't have anything to do with blood. Eulas, Lula, Alius—those bonds were stronger than any his biological family could ever offer. Those were the people he would remember when he was seventy-years-old, sitting in a cozy cottage by the fire retelling stories of magical mountains.

Eulas sat back in his chair and whispered. "I always wanted a son."

Nicholas lowered his head, his nose burning from the struggle to stay strong. "I've always needed a father."

Eulas teared up, but quickly covered by shaking off the emotion and pulling out the old pocket watch that was tucked into the pocket of his shirt, "It's almost time to go."

"Go where?"

"To celebrate Christmas Eve, of course. Grab your coat and hat, it's gonna be a cold one."

Nicholas bundled up and followed Eulas to the barn. Baret stood tall and confident with the wagon, like a proper stallion, as if he knew exactly where to go. Maybe he did. In the back corner of the barn, small sacks had been filled with potatoes, apples, and preserves made by Eulas and Nicholas. He'd assumed they were making multiple batches to put up for winter, but he was wrong. A basket held what looked to be homemade pastries, and Eulas said they were for the orphans.

After loading the wagon, Baret led them into the most congested area of Brusberg, close to the church. Brisk wind whipped across his face and the black of night hovered, anticipating Christmas morning. The first delivery went to the church, for the children at the orphanage. Eulas had prepared small bags for each child to have for Christmas, along with tasty desserts. After Eulas placed the gifts on the front steps, he knocked once, then snuck back to the safety of the wagon. Nicholas swallowed his emotion when he witnessed their reaction. This is what he'd dreamed about— Christmas for everyone.

After the first delivery, they shuffled into town, keeping Baret at a safe distance so they would go unnoticed. Eulas knew the homes that suffered the most, the families that struggled to feed their children. One by one, Nicholas watched as he placed a burlap sack of food on the doorstep and crept away without a sound. His eyes widened in excitement and he began to feel the spark that he'd once craved more than anything. The desire to be a part of something life changing.

Eulas fed around twenty houses that night, not caring that he'd limited his own food storage for the winter. When he came to the last house, Eulas pushed the sack into Nicholas's arms and patted him on the back.

"You want me to do it?" Nicholas asked.

"I do."

He stared at the door, anxiously. "What if I mess up?"

"You won't. You've watched me all night. But this time, I want you to knock and then run to that corner in the shadows. I'll be waiting for you." Eulas pointed behind his back to the tall brick building.

Nicholas peered over Eulas's shoulder, making sure he knew where to go, then nodded. He took a deep breath and turned toward the house. The roof, partially black from age and mildew, sunk in toward the front of the cottage and one of the front windows had been boarded up instead of replaced. Weeds grew haphazardly throughout the yard, reaching toward the uneven cobblestone walkway as if begging for Nicholas's attention.

His shaky hand reached toward the door knocker, and it came loose from the weathered wood as soon as he gripped it. Standing frozen, door knocker in hand, he turned to Eulas with wide eyes. Eulas motioned for him to toss it to the side and continue on. Nicholas glanced around his feet, as if there was an appropriate place for the object, but eventually tossed it into the weeds.

He placed the sack on the doorstep and once again, looked over his shoulder toward the old farmer. Eulas shooed him with his hands, hurrying him along. Nicholas took a deep breath, knocked twice, then bolted for the safety of the shadows. He could hear Eulas chuckling as he ran for his life.

"Don't think I've ever seen you move that fast, Son."

He would have answered, if he could have caught his breath. The creak of old wood resounded throughout the quiet streets as the door opened. Eulas pulled Nicholas into a squatting position alongside him and put one finger over his mouth, silently telling him not to speak. When Nicholas's gaze caught sight of the figure in the doorway, he stopped breathing. His cheeks flushed with anger as he absorbed the scowl-faced boy at the door.

Hans.

"Eulas, this boy doesn't deserve anything," he whispered. "He tortures me at school. Says horrible things about you!"

Eulas grinned. "Nicholas, I have dealt with people like him my entire life. I'm a poor, black farmer with little to my name. But I have far more self-respect than he has insults. I assure you."

"How can you give him your food? Our food?"

Eulas leaned forward, as if making sure Nicholas was listening. "Father always told me to be kind to unkind people. They need it the most." Eulas pointed toward Hans, kneeling by the small sack. Hans glanced around, sporting a sneer for anyone lurking nearby.

All of a sudden Han's eyes widened, and his face softened as he pulled the haul of apples and preserves from the sack. A youthful appearance emerged—the boy hidden underneath the protective wall of bitterness. Nicholas watched as he transformed into a hungry, vulnerable kid—much like himself when Eulas found him.

He devoured the apple as if it were the most precious thing he'd ever seen, randomly glancing over his shoulder as if someone would try to take it. Hate dissipated and sympathy took root. Hans was no more than a child himself, lost in a world of misfortune.

"You see, Nicholas. Christmas isn't about feasts, desserts or decorating the tree. While lovely, Christmas carols won't teach you what's important. Christmas is the miracle of Jesus's birth. And sometimes, these people need a miracle of their own. I can't think of anything more powerful than showing grace to someone who's done nothing to deserve it."

Nicholas's eyes filled with tears. A prezent for someone who'd done nothing but torture him. Clarity came from humbleness as he saw Hans in a different light. It wasn't about recognition. No, Hans would never know who left the selfless gift. It was about putting someone else first, no matter what they'd done.

It was about doing something bigger than yourself.

A purpose.

Nicholas had never experienced the overwhelming combination of love, gratefulness and hope like that Christmas Eve night. He'd spent most of his life yearning for the gift of Christmas spirit and praying for a family.

God answered.

He sent Eulas Klaus.

LULA

*T*he reflection of the pale, blonde-haired woman stared back—as if studying her own dim brown eyes and lackluster expression. She looked like a complete stranger, not recognizing the girl she once was. The one filled with hope and promise of a fulfilling life.

"Girl!"

Lula jolted at the gravelly screech from downstairs. No matter how many years went by, her father's voice terrified her. Even in his miserable and inadequate state.

"Girl! Where are you?"

She turned away from the small cracked mirror leaning against the wall and hustled down the narrow stairs from her loft. Mr. Brunon's thin frame sat hunched on his bed, his large eyes wider than usual, as if it would help his sight. It didn't.

"Right here, Mr. Brunon. Did you need something?"

"Selfish child. Always thinking about yourself, aren't you?"

Lula knew better than to argue. She stood silently,

waiting for his tantrum to subside. He'd give out . . . eventually.

"Worst thing I ever did, taking you in my home. I should have known better!"

She attempted to change the subject, hoping it would calm the beast within. "Would you like something to drink?"

"You don't have anything strong enough to ease the burden of your presence!"

"I understand the feeling," Lula mumbled under her breath. "If you'll excuse me, I'll start dinner."

"You better!"

Lula pulled the door closed, hoping to muffle his ramblings. Age had not been kind as far as Mr. Brunon was concerned. His inability to get around did make her life somewhat easier, but if she got within two feet of him, he'd swipe the side of her face with his cane, then cackle.

Lula stepped into the quiet narrow kitchen and breathed. This was her safe space. She could busy herself with cooking and cleaning, dreaming of a life outside of his wrath. She wasn't sure how much longer he would live, or what she would do when he passed.

As his only heir, could she inherit the home? Did she even want to? She only wanted the small box that belonged to her mother, and Lula had managed to sneak it out of the house, burying it in a safe place under the Rosemary in the herb garden. They could burn everything else to the ground. She tied the apron around her waist and busied herself in the kitchen for the next two hours, baking fresh brot and preparing sauerkraut.

She organized his tray as usual. The plate in the center, a folded cloth napkin on the left with his fork on the right. A glass of water, not too cold or not too warm, sat above the fork. If one thing lay out of place—she'd pay.

Balancing the meal on one hand, she knocked twice before entering the lair of bitterness and hate.

"Better be my food, Girl!"

Lula stepped inside the room without a word and sat the tray on the bedside table. With her eyes down, she quickly shuffled toward the door.

"Better not be consorting with the ginger dwarf if you know what's good for you. I'm watching you."

Lula was used to his ugly insults toward Alius and paid them no mind. She only wanted out of the room as soon as possible.

"Just like his parents, he is. Ugly and useless. The lot of em'."

Lula froze. His parents? How did he know his parents? She turned slowly, unable to hide the shock. "Pardon me, Sir. I thought Alius was an orphan. Did you say you knew his parents?"

His greasy smile spoke volumes. He'd gotten her attention and he knew it. "Know them? No. I don't consort with the likes of people like that."

She stepped forward, desperate for anything he had to offer. "Like what? What were they like?"

"Peasants they were. Worth no more than him."

Lula wanted to argue—stand up for her kind-hearted friend who Mr. Brunon would never compare to, but she knew there was no use. "Where are they now? Are they in Poland?"

"My food is getting cold. Stop wasting my time."

"Please, Mr. Brunon. I'm only curious."

He eyed Lula over the slice of brot, biting and chewing it leisurely as if he had all day to keep her waiting. He enjoyed it.

"I believe they left for Scotland after burying their sons."

"Their sons?"

Mr. Brunon grinned. "Both were lost at sea. They only recovered one body."

"But . . ." Lula began. "Alius is alive. They need to know he's alive. Why didn't you say something?"

Mr. Brunon shrugged. "It isn't my problem. Or yours. Remember your place, Girl."

Lula's chest tightened and tears stung her eyes at the thought of Alius's parents mourning for their son. Both of their sons. Alius's brother was dead.

"If I catch you interfering, you'll regret it. That's a promise."

"Yes, Sir."

SHE HADN'T SLEPT FOR SEVERAL DAYS. MR. BRUNON'S WORDS rolled through her mind over and over. It wasn't a secret she could keep from Alius. Plus, Mr. Brunon didn't deserve her loyalty.

Typically, the only day she and Alius were able to chat at all were Wednesdays when she ran errands for Mr. Brunon. A dark alleyway didn't seem like the place for this conversation, though. No, she needed somewhere private, that preferably didn't smell like trash.

When the second set of footsteps echoed her own, she abruptly turned into St. Mary's, knowing he would follow. The church was quiet, with only a couple of people scattered about in pews. Lula sauntered to an empty bench in the center of the church, away from the others. Within minutes, Alius had taken a seat beside her.

"Alius."

"You think people are onto us? After all these years, they have to notice a short, unattractive man following a beautiful blonde around town."

Lula giggled. "Let them wonder. It's good for the mind, and Lord knows these people need it."

Alius snorted, but caught himself before he lost control. "What's going on? This isn't our ordinary chat."

"No. No, it isn't. I have news."

"News?" Alius asked. "Don't keep me in suspense, Lu. Is it Nic?"

Lula shook her head, regretfully. "Mr. Brunon, well, he said something."

"I've told you before, Lu. You don't have to put up with him. You're seventeen-years-old and I know Father Gorski would help until you are on your feet. I'll do anything I can to get you out of there, you know that."

Lula's face softened at his words as she reached to hold his hand. "I know you would. Thank you. But, this isn't about me."

"Then, who?"

"You, Alius. Your family."

Alius froze. He shook his head and furrowed his brow in confusion. "What are you talking about?"

Lula swallowed, attempting to relieve the tightness in her throat. "Mr. Brunon has forbidden me to say anything, but I could never keep a secret from you. You know I wouldn't."

Silence.

"He said they traveled to Scotland after the accident at sea. After . . ."

"This is wonderful, Lu! I mean, they could be anywhere in Scotland, but at least I know where to start."

"Al," Lula whispered.

"You have to come with me. Ma will love you. Argos will flirt with you, but that's nothing unusual." His chuckles died off at the look of concern on Lula's face. "You don't want to come?"

"There's something else." She closed her eyes and prayed

for strength. "Mr. Brunon said they left Poland after burying their sons."

"I'm sure he was mistaken. They probably assumed I had died, ya know."

She shook her head, sadly. "He said they only recovered one body."

For a split second, time froze. Neither she or Alius blinked or breathed. Lula waited patiently for him to accept her words, as hard as they were to hear. As reality broke through denial, Alius gasped and jerked his hand away from Lula.

"He's lying. You're lying!" Alius stood and every head in the church spun their way. "Why are you doing this?"

Lula stood, but continued to whisper as if embarrassed over the scene. "I'm trying to be honest with you."

"I jumped in after Argos—pulled him to safety!"

Her face softened, in sympathy and sadness. "You said he dove back in after you."

Alius's mouth hung open in shock as a single tear rolled down his cheek. He ran his fingers through his unruly red hair and turned toward the door. Lula stepped forward to follow him, but he halted her with one hand.

She knew he needed to be alone.

Lula sat down, devastated at the thought of hurting Alius. Did she do the right thing? Would Al have been better off not knowing? She knew losing his twin brother would be difficult, but maybe it wasn't the best time to tell him. Was there ever a good time? She slipped out the doors of St. Mary's, blocking the sun from her eyes. Alius wasn't anywhere to be found. There wasn't anything for her to do. He would talk about it when ready and she couldn't push him. Times such as this were when she missed Nicholas the most. He would know how to help Alius.

Nicholas. Four years and her heart ached as if she'd lost

him the day before. Was he still in Germany? Did he think of her? She'd lost hope in her future long ago, but dreamed of a magnificent life for him. A purpose like no other.

Lula finished her errands, taking more time than usual to return home. It was always nice to drag out her minutes away from Mr. Brunon, but she also held onto the hope of seeing Alius. She worried over him.

It apparently didn't take long for Alius to feel guilty over their conversation. His heart was too soft. Lula didn't blame him for the outburst—she couldn't imagine how she would feel at that moment. When she arrived home, he'd been waiting under the large oak tree behind her cottage, knees tucked to his chest and hands clasped. He refused to look her in the eye as she eased toward him, as if approaching a wild animal.

"I'm sorry for what I said," he whispered.

Her face softened. "Alius, there's no need to apologize. I know you are in pain. What kind of friend would I be if I didn't understand that?"

He struggled to stand, his short legs pushing off the ground underneath him. "I have to go. It's too risky for me to be here, but I needed to say I'm sorry."

Lula watched him shuffle across the back yard, how one shoulder sat slightly higher than the other and how his toes angled out with every step. She knew every feature—every mannerism. There was no one like him.

"Alius?" she called out.

He turned to look over his shoulder, but he never met her gaze.

"I love you. I hope you know."

His lips tightened, then a half-grin broke through the pain. He needed those words. Berta used to say that everyone needed to hear they're loved from time to time. It feeds our soul. It reminds us that we are more than how we see ourselves.

Alius continued through the field toward Father Gorski's home and she prayed he'd find the comfort he needed with the priest. He could always shine a light on the darkest of times.

She pushed open the back door of the cottage, her arms piled high with a heavy bag of flour and fresh vegetables. The scratchy clearing of Mr. Brunon's throat caught her attention and she spun, absorbing the sight of him by the fire. Dressed in his finest suit, his frail body hunched from the effort it took to rise from his bed. Her gaze swept to the opposite side of the room to find a gentleman, possibly in his forties, studying her.

The man stood tall with authority, dressed in all brown, with a belt of metals from shoulder to hip. He held his head high as he looked down at her with curiosity. "Is this her?" One brow raised in question.

Mr. Brunon grunted. "Lula, put those away and come sit down."

Lula nodded and shuffled into the kitchen, her hands shaking from fear. What did he want? Did he have bad news? She didn't have a clue what would transpire, but a sinking feeling in the pit of her stomach told her it wasn't good. She swept her hands over her wind-blown hair and straightened her dress. Hiding all emotion, she walked blank-faced into the room.

The gentleman swept his hand toward the bench, asking her to sit.

"I'd rather stand if that's alright."

Mr. Brunon's heavy breathing could be heard across the room. "Lula, this is General Brzoska of the Polish army."

The room quieted, as if that was supposed to mean anything to her. Her expression never changed.

"And?" she asked.

Both men began to cackle, entertained by her lack of enthusiasm.

"I love her spirit. You were right about her."

Lula tilted her head. "I'm sorry. I don't believe I understand."

"General Brzoska has offered a dowry for you, Lula. One I cannot refuse at my age. My time is near and you have no options."

"A dowry?" Lula shook her head and stepped back in shock.

"That's right," General Brzoska replied. "You are to be my wife."

15

NICHOLAS

*N*icholas sat in the back corner of the barn, whittling the thick log as if his life depended on it. It had taken a few years to persuade Eulas, but he'd finally relented. This year, along with the preserves, apples and danishes, the children would each receive a special gift. For some it might be a handmade toy, and others a pair of mittens or toboggan from Minna.

Seeing the enthusiasm on the children's faces was Nicholas's favorite thing in the world. Most were more excited over food than anything, but why not give them both? After Eulas agreed, he began carving an old wooden wagon and horses for Nicholas to use as an example. The lines were perfectly balanced on both sides and the detail of the horse's snout astounded him.

It reminded him of the doll Alius created.

"That doesn't look like a horse. Is it supposed to?" Minna asked.

Nicholas paused, glaring at her over his task. "Don't you have something to do?"

"Nothing as entertaining." She snickered.

Minna had taken a position at the orphanage when she finished school, assisting with daily chores and cooking. She still managed to hound him whenever possible, although not as often as she used to. Nicholas was content on the farm and Eulas was proud to have him, especially since the past few years had taken a toll on his body.

Nicholas couldn't imagine being anywhere else.

"You only have a few more weeks until Christmas. You'll never finish in time," she mumbled.

He continued carving into the dense wood and muttered, "I'll finish."

"I knitted a new red cap for you. Did you know? It is a tradition and your large head grew out of the last one."

"I'm so thankful I have you, Minna. Who else would insult and keep me humble?"

Minna grinned mischievously, stood, and shook the hay from her skirt. She took a deep breath, then faltered as if something was on her mind. As she stared at him, sadness swept across the room like a storm. She didn't have to speak, he could feel it.

"Are you alright?" she asked. "You seem sad."

"Just thinking about Eulas, that's all."

Minna focused on the dirt underneath her boot, refusing to meet his gaze. "You never really talk about him. I've wanted to ask, but I felt as though I was intruding on something . . . sacred. Does that make sense?"

Nicholas knew Eulas was a man who liked his privacy. He never left the farm and the past six months or so, he had slowed physically, as if his mind and body were dwindling. He never felt the need to include anyone on the details of their relationship—it was a special bond between the two of them.

"It does make sense. Thank you, Minna."

She sighed, giving up on his reply. "I've left a pot of stew on the porch. If you can eat a bite, maybe it will help."

Nicholas nodded, but didn't respond. The thought of losing Eulas sent him into a panic. He couldn't even breathe. Shudders of emotion built inside his chest and the slightest movement would tip him over the edge. Eulas was the only family he had.

Minna turned away. Before closing the door behind her, she whispered, "You know I'm here for you. If you need anything—you're never alone. I hope you know that." Then the old barn door closed, leaving him with the chickens and Franz.

Minna was a loyal friend. At one point in his life, he feared she wanted more, but thankfully she never pursued a romantic relationship. They were too much alike—more brother and sister than anything. Even so, his heart belonged to another and it always would. Minna knew his history with Lula and she respected his affection for her.

The uneven, botched face of the wooden horse glared back as if appalled by Nicholas's handywork. He could make them for the Christmas sacks—if he wanted to terrify the small children of Brusberg. He tossed the carving into the hay and stood from the cold floor of the barn. His back and shoulders ached from his hunched position on the ground, and he stretched—alleviating tight, coiled muscles. He checked on the animals before making his way inside to Eulas, all except Heidi. That huhn never let go of her hatred for him and he avoided her at all costs.

The last few months hadn't been easy. Eulas's energy depleted more and more until he resorted to mid-day naps and turning in early in the evenings. He'd never seen anyone go downhill so quickly. Nicholas would watch as he'd push his food from one side of the plate to the other, his lack of appetite obvious.

If he caught Nicholas staring, Eulas would distract him with stories of his youth, as if protecting him from what lay ahead. But Nicholas knew. He wasn't a young, naive boy anymore and he understood the harsh reality of life.

Eulas didn't have much time.

He hadn't given much thought as to what would happen when Eulas passed. No, he would rather cherish every second with the selfless soul who'd molded him into the person he'd become. The man who saved his life and taught him what truly mattered at the end of the day.

As Nicholas left the barn, movement across the field caught his attention. He shielded his eyes from the dim gleam of sunlight shining through the clouds. As he walked closer, he saw Eulas sitting underneath the old birch tree, rocking back and forth as if singing to himself. Nicholas almost turned back to give him space—almost.

"No need to spy on an old man. Come, take a load off," Eulas called out.

Nicholas smiled and walked forward, easing down into the snow-covered ground beside him. "Should have brought a blanket, Eulas. You're liable to catch a cold sitting out here."

Eulas chuckled. "A cold is the last thing I'm worried about."

Nicholas didn't reply—he knew the old man wouldn't listen anyway. They sat together in silence while absorbing the beautiful sight of winter on the farm. He studied the old birch tree rising from the plain of dense white snow. The thick trunk split low to the ground, branching out into several smaller trunks, it's bark a unique combination of gray and white. The limbs soared high into the air, hovering over them from the weight of new-fallen snow.

"Eulas? Tell me about Alma."

Eulas's face softened at the mention of her name. "I met Alma at the age of thirteen. Her mama died young and her papa kept her close to home. He hardly let her out of the house.

But sometimes, he would help Daddy on the farm, and he'd always bring Alma. My parents, Ron and Joy, had a place like this and when chores were done, me and Alma would sneak off, swimming or taking walks in the fields."

Eulas elbowed him as if proud of his rebellious youth.

"She always wore white, except for that red scarf—her mama's scarf. Tied around her head, neck, or even around her waist, she never left home without it. Told her she'd be buried with it one day, but she refused. Wanted it to go to someone else that needed it's comfort. Maybe someone like her without a mama."

He turned toward Nicholas. "Her Papa had an accident when she turned seventeen, and after he passed, she had nowhere to go. So, we decided to marry."

"Just like that? It seems like a big decision."

Eulas smiled, "When you know, you know. Said our vows in the church, but later that night when we were all alone, we snuck out here to do it again—just the two of us. We loved this tree. The strength and beauty . . . we admired all that it stood for. Some of the best years of my life were spent on this farm with Alma. It's been hard without her."

"I'm sorry, Eulas. I shouldn't have asked."

"No need to be sorry. I can talk about that woman all day, Son."

"I know what that's like, or at least, I used to," Nicholas admitted.

Eulas nodded. "You will again one day. Don't ever lose faith in the power of love, Nicholas. Those difficult roads can lead to magical destinations."

A FEW DAYS LATER, NICHOLAS FOUND HIMSELF SITTING UNDER the tree alone, pondering Eulas's words. He envied his peaceful nature. Eulas carried a calm spirit that few people were born with. Nicholas stood, needing to return home to check on him. Everyday, the light in his eyes dimmed a little more.

Nicholas reached for the door, but paused at the deep soulful timbre of Eulas singing 'Holy God, We Praise Thy Name'. That voice . . . he absorbed every note. Time itself seemed to slow for Nicholas to relish every second. He turned and leaned against the cottage wall, sliding down to the floor of the porch. Eyes closed, he sang the words he'd heard on many late nights with the stars gleaming overhead. Eulas's most cherished hymn.

When the song ended, Nicholas sat in silence thinking of all he needed to say. He stood, pushing open the door, and eased into the small cottage he knew as home. Eulas laid on his back, staring up at the planks of the ceiling—perhaps in another time and place. Nicholas wondered what went through his mind at that moment. Happy memories? Regrets? It could have been his mule, Baret, for all he knew.

Eulas's gaze found Nicholas and he smirked. "How's Heidi?"

"Hateful." Nicholas pulled a chair from the table and sat beside his bed. "I mean, how long can a chicken live?"

Eulas's deep chuckle reverberated throughout the cottage. "I'll never forget the day you ran from the barn with that huhn on your head." Laughter turned into painful wheezing as he threw his hand over his chest. "You've brought so much happiness to my final years, Son. Hard to imagine a time without you now."

Nicholas cleared his throat. "I can't imagine my life without you."

Eulas reached for his hand and gripped it like a lifeline. "I need to talk with you."

"We don't have to do this right now, Eulas. You need to eat—it might help."

"You're my son, through and through." Eulas paused to make sure he understood. "In the back corner of the barn, you'll find a hidden latch on the floor. There's a box with my life savings. Our earnings, Son. It's rightfully yours."

"I don't expect anything, Eulas. You've given me more than you'll ever know."

"And that's why you deserve it. Save it, use it—it's up to you. One day a pretty little thing is going to come along and you'll have a family of your own. Maybe build a nice, respectable home. I'm proud to have a part in that."

"Thank you, Eulas."

"One more thing. The deed, dated on the day you arrived, is there—where I sold the farm to you. There's nothing I want more than to keep it in the family."

"But, you didn't even know me then."

Eulas grinned. "I knew."

Nicholas teared up, then shook his head and smiled as if he were being ridiculous. "Look at me. Eighteen-years-old and I'm still crying."

"Tears are more powerful than a thousand words. Don't ever be ashamed of showing someone how you feel. You'll never regret it."

"Yes, Sir."

"I want you to promise me something."

"Anything."

"Never lose your Christmas spirit, Nicholas. It's special and these children deserve their miracle. Promise me."

He nodded. "I promise."

There was so much he wanted to say, but wasn't sure where to start. "I want to thank you. For saving my life.

Giving me a home. For Christmas. I'm not sure I can do it without you, Eulas. You are the heart and soul of our Christmas Eve adventures. I'm still the orphan you found on the shore that day, just a few years older."

"You're no orphan, Nicholas. You're my boy. It's not who you are that holds you back, it's who you think you're not."

Nicholas sat frozen, processing Eulas's words. He wanted to be more, he truly did. From a young age, he dreamed of living out his purpose with the love of his life. Everything fell apart and he got lost along the way. Until Eulas found him.

"I want to believe that, I do," Nicholas replied. "I'm losing everyone I've ever loved."

"Your life is not lost, Son. You can marry—have a family of your own. Don't let your past dictate your future. Every minute of your life, you have the power to determine how your story will end. Remember that."

Nicholas listened, taking in every smidgen of wisdom Eulas had gained over the years. He would never be as wise or selfless, but he'd always strive to be someone Eulas would be proud of.

Eulas's eyes dimmed. "I always wondered why I was still here, still in this world while my Alma was gone. Did the Lord not want me? Then I realized, it's because my work wasn't done. I was here for you, Nicholas. But you don't need me anymore."

Nicholas shook his head, disagreeing. "I do. I do need you," he cried.

"I'm thankful for the extra time, Son. But now it's time for me to move on." Eulas took a deep breath. "I won't put you through this. It isn't something you need to see and I want you to remember me as I am right now."

"But, where will you go?"

"Don't you worry about that. I have it all figured out." Eulas smiled.

Nicholas exhaled and tears ran down his cheeks. Eulas was tired, and he deserved peace. "I love you, Eulas."

"Love you, Nicholas."

. . .

THE EARLY MORNING SUN HAD JUST BEGUN TO PEEK OVER THE mountainside—not quite enough to wake Nicholas from slumber, although something did. He sat up, stretched his arms high above his head, and yawned.

He couldn't go back to sleep at that point . . . trying was futile. Winter had brought a fresh wave of new fallen snow, and blanketed the farm in white silk.

Beautiful.

One of Eulas's most beloved views was a glorious winter snow, and he could only imagine the sparkle in the old man's eyes when he caught sight of it.

"Eulas, you have to see this."

Silence.

Nicholas turned away from the window and eased toward the bed. "Eulas? Are you awake?"

Silence.

There was no reply—no movement of any kind. Only a small scrap of paper laying in the center of the bed. His chest tightened and he felt as if he'd be sick. He shook his head from side to side, in denial at what he already knew.

The first thing he did was run to the small bedside table where Alma's scarf and his father's pocket watch always lay. They were gone.

"No. Please, no." He gripped the thin paper in his hand that read, 'Always keep the spirit.' A tortured cry of pain filled the cottage. A heart-wrenching shout of emotion consumed with grief. "Please don't leave me," he shouted to no one.

Nicholas tortured himself with regrets—things he should have told him. Did he truly know how he felt? He had no idea how long he sat there. Talking, praying, crying. He drifted in and out of consciousness, and at one point he swore he felt Eulas's hand on his shoulder—comforting him.

Nicholas stumbled from the cottage as if he could stop him, tell him to come back so he could take care of him the way he had done Nicholas. He ran barefoot through the snow, ignoring the bite of icy flakes on the soles of his feet.

Eulas was gone.

Nicholas fell to his knees and tilted his head back toward the sky in tears. He thanked God for the time he was given with Eulas Klaus, then the softest of flurries began to fall, melting against his face.

As if being kissed by the Heavens.

. . .

2 Weeks Later

THE SECOND WEEK WITHOUT EULAS PROVED HARDER THAN THE first. Nicholas prepared dinner every night, imagining Eulas beside him—lecturing him on the proper way to cook fish. They'd bicker, then eventually laugh at the other's stubbornness. But when Nicholas would turn to offer another helping, Eulas's chair sat empty—his fish untouched.

Those nights were the hardest.

The spirit of the farm had vanished, as if the peaceful energy around him dissipated. The world felt colder—harder without him. The animals went about their normal routine, although without motivation. Heidi no longer cared enough to be disgruntled. The high-pitched squeals from Franz's pen had been silenced. Even Baret refused to eat.

Nicholas continued his chores as if nothing was amiss. He spread fresh hay, cut firewood, and collected eggs as usual. His own private bubble of denial—and he would have stayed there if he hadn't been interrupted.

"Nicholas?"

He didn't turn around or acknowledge Minna in any way.

"Nicholas, what are you doing?"

He seethed. Her question alone brought forth an unrecognizable anger he'd never experienced. "What does it look like?"

She stepped forward, the small crunch of hay under her petite boot fueling his annoyance. "It's just, well, you're out here everyday. Everything is cleaned and stocked. Is there a point in all of this?"

"Just because you don't understand it doesn't mean there isn't a point."

"Look, Nicholas. I know . . ."

"You don't know anything!" Nicholas shook his head and inhaled through his nose. "Please leave."

Minna didn't respond—only spun on her heels, letting the barn door slam behind her. He tilted his head back and closed his eyes, attempting to rein in his temper. It wasn't Minna's fault. Nicholas only had one week until Christmas and he made a promise to Eulas. How would he ever manage without him?

Once again, the hinges of the barn door squeaked loudly and Nicholas balled his fist in rage. "I told you to leave!"

"Tell me how you really feel, Nic."

Nicholas spun, but couldn't respond. He stared at his best friend. Yes, he was older, but he'd recognize the short-statured, red-haired man anywhere. It was truly Alius.

"Am I going crazy?" Nicholas asked. "Is it really you?"

"Know anyone else as handsome as this? I think not."

Nicholas hurried across the barn and wrapped his arms around Alius. He gripped the back of his coat, afraid he'd disappear if he released him. The relief of his survival, along with the grief of losing Eulas, crashed around him and he collapsed to his knees.

"You drowned. I watched you fall from the boat and the waves took you."

Alius pulled away to look him in the eyes. "Luckily we were close enough to shore for the storm to bring me in. Father Gorski found me that night."

"You've been with him all this time?" Nicholas asked. "All these years?" Surely his best friend would have let him know he was alive. Wouldn't he?

Alius frowned and guilt filled his eyes. "I'm sorry, Nic. Lula wanted to set you free. She thought it best if you stayed away or else they would've locked you up. I kept the address from your letter, just in case."

"Lula?" The betrayal of her lies stung, even if she did have good intentions. It didn't matter. Nothing she could say would ever change the way he felt about her.

Alius exhaled. "I have so much to tell you."

16

NICHOLAS

"*L*ook, Nic, I'll sleep on the floor. I imagine it's painful for someone else to sleep in Mr. Klaus's bed."

Nicholas fluffed the pillow and pulled a fresh blanket across the bed. "It's fine, Al. You can have my bed and I'll sleep in his."

Alius pursed his lips and shuffled from foot to foot, uncomfortably. "Only if you're sure."

"I'm sure." Nicholas faced him with his hands on his hips and attempted a comforting smile. "I'm really sorry about Argos. You have your own pain, you know." Nicholas knew nothing would ease the heartache of losing a loved one. Nothing except time.

Alius cleared his throat and ran his fingers through his wiry hair. "At least I have an idea where Ma and Pa are. That's something. I asked around town and a neighbor remembered the name of Ma's sister—she thinks they could have gone there. I wrote to my Aunt Aly and Uncle Gary just in case."

"I hope you find them, Alius. I really do."

Alius studied him. "You're a big bloke, you are. Always

knew you would be," he mumbled. "But there's something different about you. The innocence is gone, and there's a presence I didn't expect. Strong and demanding, but still —you."

"What did you think you'd find?" Nicholas asked.

Alius focused on his feet, unable to meet the intense blue eyes of his oldest friend. "I don't know, the boy searching for his purpose? Instead, I found a man with one."

Nicholas sat on the edge of the bed, and leaned forward in thought. "The last few years on Christmas Eve night, well, it changed something inside of me. Witnessing the hungry and broken grab hold of a few seconds of wonder, a gift I took part in, was like nothing I've ever experienced."

"Sounds like you found your spirit," Alius whispered.

"I can't imagine doing it without Eulas."

Alius's eyes widened. "You have to. You promised him."

Nicholas sat quietly, remembering his last conversation with Eulas. Christmas was less than a week away. Could he do it?

As if reading his mind, Alius spoke up, "I'll help you, but then you have to do something for me. Actually, for Lula."

Nicholas straightened. "Lula? Is she alright?"

"Mr. Brunon is selling her to some general, Nic. He's receiving a hefty dowry for her hand. Lula is devastated."

Nicholas stood and began pacing the small cottage floor. He had struggled with Lula's letter of rejection, but never gave up the notion that she belonged with him. No, this man would never get his hands on her—he'd make sure of it.

"When?" Nicholas asked.

"New Year's Eve. We don't have much time. I know I should have come sooner, but I wasn't sure how you'd react or if you'd even want to help after you received her letter."

Nicholas paused with his brows raised in shock. "Of course I'll help. She doesn't deserve to be anyone's property and I don't hold anything against either of you. How could I?"

"I hoped you would say that."

THE NEXT COUPLE OF DAYS, NICHOLAS AND ALIUS PACKED small burlap sacks with leftover potatoes and stored apples from the fall harvest. Nicholas expected Minna to arrive at any moment with pastries and felt somewhat embarrassed over his behavior earlier in the week. Shuffling and grunting from the corner of the barn pulled Nicholas from his state of guilt.

Alius squirmed, obviously uncomfortable by the narrowing of his eyes and wrinkled nose. His hands searched the hay underneath him and eventually pulled the wooden horse free from the straw.

"Blimey, Nic. What happened to this?"

Nicholas glared. "I was—practicing."

"Practicing for what? Murder? Torture?" Alius's mouth hung open at the apparent lack of wood-carving talent. "Are you trying to terrify the children?"

"If you're so brilliant, have at it," Nicholas mumbled.

Alius continued studying the horrible excuse for a toy. "How many houses do you visit?"

"Maybe fifty or so. The first year we delivered around fifteen, but the need in Brusberg has grown substantially."

Nicholas looked up from his burlap sack at Alius's lack of response. His mouth hung open in shock and something that looked like admiration.

"It's not as bad as it sounds," Nicholas added.

Silence.

"Al?"

He followed Al's gaze outside the barn door where Minna

shuffled through the snow, her arms filled with boxes of homemade desserts. The curls of her long brown hair blew across her face as she fought to see in front of her. Nicholas's eyes traveled back to Alius's and he grinned at the smitten expression on his friend's face. Alius was lost.

"Alright there, Al?"

Alius didn't respond, but jumped from his sitting position and rushed toward the beautiful damsel. Only a few feet away from the entrance, Minna stumbled forward and Alius reached out to catch her, saving her and the pastries from devastation.

Minna's head snapped up within inches of Alius's and their eyes locked. Nicholas leaned against the barn door with his arms crossed over his chest, grinning at the obvious connection between the two.

Minna stood over a foot taller than Alius, slender and graceful—the bottom of her skirt wet from walking in the snow. Alius, quite pudgy around the middle, smiled a toothy grin and took the packages from her arms.

Minna threw her hand over her chest and gasped. "Oh, my. What a gentleman you are."

"Only when there is a beautiful lady such as yourself."

Minna giggled.

Nicholas rolled his eyes.

Alius, with an exaggerated strut, carried the boxes into the barn and wagged his brows at Nicholas as he passed. Minna hesitantly stepped in front of Nicholas, staring at the ground as if uncertain of their relationship. He knew he had to fix things between them.

"I'm really sorry, Minna. Pain is not an excuse for treating someone poorly. Please forgive me."

Minna wrapped her arms around him and held tight. "I forgave you before you asked. Pain may not be an excuse, but friends understand nonetheless."

"Now . . ." She pulled away and clapped her hands. "Who is that stump of love I met outside?"

Just like that, all was forgotten. Isn't that the way it's supposed to be? People make mistakes. No one is perfect. The people that love you no matter what—the ones who hold on to the good and brush off the bad—that's family. Minna was a part of Nicholas's family.

"Do you remember me telling you about Alius?"

Minna's eyes widened and he feared they'd pop from their sockets. "That's Alius? He's alive? Oh, Nicholas, this is wonderful!"

"I think he may fancy you," Nicholas whispered.

Minna ran her hands down her hair and blushed. "Really? I guess I didn't think I would have a chance. He's so . . . dazzling."

"Dazzling." Nicholas repeated. He chewed his lip wondering if anyone had referred to Al as dazzling before. He didn't think so, but he loved that she saw him that way.

"Do you remember the first day we met?" Minna asked. "I told you that you would owe me a favor one day." She nodded toward the barn where Alius unloaded supplies.

Nicholas raised his brows.

"So," Alius called out. "I'm going to start on the children's toys while you finish the sacks. Alius rolled his sleeves up as if the magical talent of sculpting was soon to sweep Minna off her feet. He winked and nodded her way. "You're welcome to watch."

Minna giggled and hurried across the barn, eager to see Alius in action.

THE THREE SPENT THE NEXT FEW DAYS PREPARING FOR THE biggest Christmas Eve Nicholas had ever organized in Brusberg. Somehow, Alius managed to carve over fifty flawless wooden toys for the children in town. Soldiers, trains, animals—he truly held an artistic gift Nicholas lacked and couldn't comprehend.

The wagon sat in the barn, fully loaded with Baret anxiously shuffling from hoof to hoof. It was the first time since Eulas's death the mule had acted like himself. Maybe it would be good for all of them. Nicholas sat on an old wooden stool, his eyes traveling over the load of gifts for the city. He could imagine the twinkle in the old man's eye—the grin, full of anticipation, that he always reserved for Christmas Eve night.

After delivering gifts to Brusberg, Nicholas had organized a local captain to travel by boat to Dalbeca for Lula. She would be with him by Christmas morning—he refused to return home without her.

Nicholas looked up toward the sky. "Stay with me tonight, Eulas. I need you."

There wasn't a whisper of reassurance or wind of comfort. Nothing that would convince anyone he had been heard, but Nicholas never doubted it. Eulas would always be with him.

The dark, peaceful town of Brusberg, dimly lit by candles in the cottage windows, felt solemn. As if the city itself mourned the first holiday without their own Eulas Klaus. Nicholas felt it as well.

Minna and Alius sat beside him in the loaded wagon, just having finished their deliveries to the orphanage. It was Alius's first—an eye-opening experience that left him not only speechless, but emotional as well. The orphans were delighted with Alius's wood carvings and he promised there would be more next year. He sat on the floor watching their excitement over the simple toys, and Nicholas knew the sense of pride he felt by bringing joy to those innocent children. It wasn't that many years ago that they were on the other side of those doors, in need of their own miracle.

House to house, the three of them made their way across town, surprising hungry families with treats galore. Most of the time, they would continue on to the next house, but Nicholas pulled Minna and Alius into the shadows to watch a few of the special homes—just like Eulas did for him.

Alius and Minna needed to witness the children's eyes brighten like beacons in the night. A smile spreading across the face of a poor soul when all they knew was sadness and hardship—the profound difference they could make. Minna stood with her hand covering her mouth for fear of crying, while Alius held her hand.

On the way back to the barn, no one uttered a word. Nicholas remembered his first Christmas Eve, the emotions he felt afterward. It was the first Christmas he hadn't felt lost or confused. He imagined Alius and Minna needed time to process it all.

After arriving at the barn, Minna led Baret to his pen for food and water while Alius helped Nicholas store the wagon. All of a sudden, Alius spun toward Nicholas.

"I want to stay."

Nicholas's head jerked up, surprised at the outburst. "Stay? In Brusberg?"

Alius nodded.

"Does this have anything to do with a curly hair beauty outside the barn?" Nicholas asked.

Alius bit his lip. "It's everything. Minna, Christmas, you. I've never felt so useful or worthy of a future." He shrugged bashfully. "Maybe a future with Minna."

"You've always been worthy, Al. I'd love nothing more than for you to stay. You know that."

Alius grinned. "I'll need to gather my things. Say goodbye to Father Gorski when we go back. He's been so good to me."

Nicholas was thrilled at having Alius back in his life and wanted nothing more than for him to stay. "We need to leave as soon as possible."

"Can I come?" Minna called out from the door.

Both men turned toward the barn door where Minna stood, wringing her hands nervously.

"Of course. Someone has to be in charge." Nicholas grinned.

A DENSE FOG, AS THICK AS HE'D EVER SEEN, HOVERED OVER THE icy water of the Baltic Sea. In a few hours, the sun would rise over the mountainside, waking the small town of Dalbeca—including a few residents he didn't intend on running into. As the familiar old pier broke through the cloudy haze of night, memories of Lula screaming, reaching for Nicholas, barraged his mind. He looked over his shoulder at Alius and exhaled.

"I think you and Minna should go ahead to Father Gorski's cottage. Say your goodbyes to him. I'll go after Lula."

"What if you need our help? What if you get into trouble?"

"I'll be less likely to be seen if it's just me."

Alius shook his head, intent on staying with his best friend.

"I won't come back without her. You have my word," Nicholas promised.

He didn't wait for Alius's reply. Jumping from the side of the boat onto the dock, Nicholas jogged to the tree-line that he knew would lead to Mr. Brunon's cottage. Whether from age or determination, the distance didn't feel as difficult as before. He kept a steady pace until the dim gleam of lanterns pulled his attention to the center of the city.

Nicholas crept from house to house, staying low to the ground and out of sight. The quiet little town slept peacefully, no doubt preparing for Christmas festivities the following day. When Mr. Brunon's cottage rose up behind the untrimmed trees and shrubs, Nicholas paused at the sight of an assigned officer guarding the front door. The general was protecting his betrothed. Nicholas snuck around to the back of the house to find a way inside—hopefully unseen.

The yellow glow of candlelight from upstairs caught his attention and he froze as his eyes traveled to the window above. Lula, donning a white lace veil, stared into a cracked mirror, crying in the middle of the night. He didn't know what he expected. Maybe the same girl that had been pulled from his boat on the sea?

This was no girl. Pale wavy hair draped across the young woman's petite shoulders. Pink flushed her high cheekbones and her full bottom lip trembled from emotion. She was the most beautiful thing he'd ever seen.

Her sadness surrounded him and he kicked himself for not coming back sooner. He should have known she didn't mean a word of that letter—everything she'd ever done was to protect him. But who has protected her?

He dug through several inches of snow, searching for a pebble large enough to make noise, but small enough to not break the glass of the window. When he found what he was looking for, he tossed the rock toward the window. The ping jolted Lula and she spun toward the glass, frightened.

Nicholas plastered himself against the side of the house, staying hidden from the officer on duty. He waited, knowing Lula would investigate the noise. The girl had always been as curious as a cat. After a few minutes, the hinges of the back door creaked slowly, as if nerves kept her hesitant from stepping outside.

"Hello?" Lula called out. "Is someone there?"

The crunch of boots grew louder and when she walked close enough to where he was hiding, Nicholas jumped out and grabbed her from behind, putting one hand over her mouth to keep her silent. He pulled her against the side of the house and stood perfectly still to make sure he hadn't drawn unwanted attention.

"Stay quiet," he whispered. "Do you understand?"

Lula's chest heaved and she nodded her head in agreement. The last thing he wanted to do was startle her, but it was more important for them to stay silent.

Nicholas spun her, placing her back against the cottage, but kept his hand over her mouth until she could see who held her captive. Lula's eyes widened, then filled with tears. Her hand covered his and she slowly pulled it from her mouth, down to the base of her neck.

"Nicholas," she whispered. "Is it really you?"

His face softened at her words. "It's me. It's time to come home, Lula. Where you belong."

She shook her head, almost in panic. "There's so much I need to tell you."

"You don't. I know enough." He brushed a stray hair the wind had blown across her cheek to the side, then grazed her skin with his fingers. "I'm going to get you out of here."

"If they catch you," she began.

"They won't."

"If they do . . ."

"I don't care, Lula. You belong with me and we both know it. We've always known it."

Lula froze from fear. Nicholas could see how Mr. Brunon

had conditioned her into thinking she deserved this abusive life. He would show her differently.

"Lula—do you trust me?"

She exhaled and grinned before answering. "With my life."

Loud footsteps marched around the house and Nicholas covered her body with his own, keeping her out of sight. He held his breath as the soldier entered through the back door, apparently making his nightly rounds.

As soon as he entered the house, Nicholas pulled her toward him. "We have to hurry."

"Nicholas, wait! My mother's box."

Lula rushed toward the herb garden and began digging until she pulled a small wooden box from underneath the snow and dirt. He didn't ask if she needed anything else from the house. They needed to get out of there as soon as possible, and the officer would soon realize Lula was gone. Nicholas grabbed her hand and they ran toward the main road so they wouldn't leave tracks through the field.

They ran as if their lives depended on it. If Lula struggled to keep up, she didn't let on. Nicholas knew the adrenaline kept them both going and fifty feet from Father Gorski's cottage, he could see the swarming of lights around Mr. Brunon's house. Lanterns.

They were searching for her.

Alius and Minna stood outside the house, anxiously keeping watch for their return. Alius ran toward Lula and enveloped her in his arms, but Nicholas wanted everyone inside as soon as possible. He continued pushing them through the front door, out of sight. Father Gorski froze at the sight of Nicholas.

"Heavens, Son. I hardly recognized you." Father Gorski chuckled. "Still stirring up trouble, are you?"

"Only when it's important, Sir." Nicholas grinned and

embraced the priest, another kind soul that had changed his life along the way.

"We need to get her out of here," Nicholas explained. "They've noticed she's gone."

Father Gorski's face fell. "A betrothal to a general is not something to take lightly, Nicholas. From what I understand, the dowry has been paid."

Nicholas sighed and closed his eyes as if praying for wisdom.

"I wish I had better advice, Son. The only thing that could halt him is if she was already . . ."

"Married," Nicholas finished. He turned his head toward Lula and grinned. "If she already has a husband."

"Well, yes," Father Gorski replied. "Of course, Mr. Brunon would be forced to repay the dowry."

The room grew silent and everyone held their breath as Nicholas kneeled before Lula and smiled.

"We knew it would always come to this. The where and when doesn't matter as long as I get to spend the rest of my life with you. Lula Faith Dunivant, will you marry me?"

Lula threw her hand over her mouth as tears filled her dark brown eyes. She placed her hands on the side of his face and nodded. "The answer has always been yes." Lula leaned forward, gently brushing her lips against his.

Nicholas stood, swinging her around the small cottage as she giggled. Rushed or not, it was the happiest day of his life. He would vow, on that Christmas day, to love and protect her as he always said he would.

Minna hurried over beside Lula and gripped her hand tightly. "Hello, I'm Minna. Your maid of honor." Minna gave a little wave as Lula's eyes widened in surprise.

Father Gorski shook his head and smiled. "We need to hurry. Any chance you have a ring?"

Nicholas cut his eyes toward Lula. "Do you have the first

ring I gave you?" He chuckled at the thought of getting married with the rusty wire around her finger. "I promise to buy you the perfect ring when I can."

Her eyes brightened. "I do have it, but I would love to wear this if it's okay. It would mean so much to me." Lula pulled the garnet and emerald band from her mother's box and held it between her fingers.

Nicholas's face softened. "Of course. It's perfect, Lula."

Father Gorski stood in front of them in the small cottage, bible in hand. "I've never married someone outside of church before, so I'm quite out of my element." He smiled and began to pray over the couple, asking for God's grace and protection over the union as they vowed to love each other for better or for worse.

Nicholas slipped her mother's ring on her finger and his heart swelled at the glimmer of pride in Lula's eyes at the sight of it.

Father Gorski turned toward Nicholas and Lula. "I now pronounce you, Mr. and Mrs. Nicholas Dalb—"

"Klaus." Nicholas interrupted.

Father Gorski paused, then smiled his approval.

"Mr. and Mrs. Nicholas Klaus."

Part

Three

17

NICHOLAS

"*I* now pronounce you husband and wife. You may kiss the bride." Father Gorski closed his bible and clutched it to his chest.

Nicholas lost himself in the smitten expression on Lula's face. Love and hope shined from his wife's eyes and there were few things in his eighteen years that could compare.

He gently tilted her chin up and slowly leaned forward. Right before his lips touched hers, they smiled. Nicholas hovered, breathing her in. "No regrets?" he asked.

"Shut up and kiss me," Lula responded. She ran her fingers through the back of his wavy hair and pulled him toward her.

The kiss started abrupt and full of excitement, similar to their first when he proposed. But it soon turned soft and sensual as the reality of what they'd done settled. They were married.

Husband and wife.

Father Gorski cleared his throat, as if uncomfortable by the blatant display of affection. Lula's small hands pushed against Nicholas's chest, breaking the moment. Minna sniffled from the corner, while Alius held her hand and grinned. At once, a pounding on the front door shattered the reunion they had waited so long for. The priest took a deep breath and nodded toward Nicholas. He knew exactly who stood on the other side.

Upon opening the door, General Brzoska stood in front of three guards. He nodded once toward the priest out of respect, then stepped forward without invitation. His eyes narrowed as he scanned the room, searching for his betrothed.

"Your father feared you'd run off so he sent for me. I assured him you would never run away from your duty. Come. I will escort you back to your father's cottage. It isn't proper for my future wife to be out this late without a guard." General Brzoska held his hand out for her.

Lula stood straighter—more determined. "I'm not going back."

"Pardon?" He tilted his head to the side, as if confused.

Nicholas stepped in front of Lula, protectively. "She isn't going anywhere." He crossed his arms over his chest and glared, meeting the general in height and stature.

The general chuckled. "And who are you?" He looked over his shoulder at his guards and laughed as if Nicholas's words were comical, but the guards shuffled from foot to foot, sensing confrontation.

"Her husband," Nicholas answered.

General Brzoska turned to face him while studying his eyes for the truth. "She is to be my wife."

Father Gorski's calm voice broke through the awkwardness. "I can assure you that he speaks the truth, General Brzoska. I married them myself."

The guards stepped back, as if refusing to interfere with holy vows made before God. The general met Nicholas's eyes. "You married this woman, knowing a dowry had been paid?"

"I don't know what you're talking about, General Brzoska. Lula accepted my proposal at the age of twelve. Now, we are officially husband and wife."

"And the dowry?" he asked.

"Sounds like Mr. Brunon's problem to me," Nicholas answered.

General Brzoska stepped forward, his gaze darting from Nicholas to Lula. "And you? Do you love him?"

Lula shuffled from foot to foot, as if nervous, and her small voice cracked as she whispered, "With all of my heart."

General Brzoska's expression was unreadable as silence consumed the cottage. Stepping toward Nicholas, he lowered his voice. "Take care of her. She deserves more than life has given thus far. You promise me that—I'll leave here without returning."

Nicholas was speechless. Hidden behind the menacing glare and thin-lipped grimace, the general was actually a decent man. "I promise."

After nodding, he looked toward Lula once more, then spun on his heel and led the others out the door.

Father Gorski pressed against the door with both hands, closing it behind the soldiers. As he turned to face them, something that looked like fear crossed his face. Not for himself, but for Nicholas and Lula.

"You need to leave—as soon as possible. As much as I would love some time with you, her father will not let her go without a fight."

Nicholas held his hand out in appreciation, but the priest smiled and enveloped him in a hug. "I always knew you'd grow up to be a great man. You've made me proud."

He wanted to respond, but couldn't find the words.

Father Gorski whispered, "Take care of them."

"With my life," he promised.

Alius took a few minutes to say a proper goodbye to the man who saved his life. Nicholas watched as Al focused on the ground while Father Gorski whispered a prayer over the boy that he'd grown close to. It reminded him of his relationship with Eulas. The crew quickly gathered their belongings and hurried toward Benson's boat at the shoreline.

Nicholas gripped Lula's hand as he scanned the forest for threats. He led the others down the narrow dock where Benson waited. He refused to fail—not this time. After boarding the boat, Nicholas quickly pulled the rope free and pushed the boat away from the dock. The quaint town of Dalbeca grew smaller as he wrapped his arms around Lula and kissed the top of her head.

Then—something in the distance moved. A subtle shadow between two tall trees lurked, watching them. Nicholas squinted his eyes, focusing on the darkness. Stepping forward out of the hidden canopy, Lula's father stood alone, waving his cane high above his head, shouting obscenities. Nicholas's grip tightened around Lula, protecting her.

Nicholas could feel the anger radiating from the shoreline—the hate they had grown accustomed to from the old man. Lula gasped as Mr. Brunon's momentum knocked him off balance, and he tumbled to the ground, rolling down the sandy shore, cursing along the way.

Lula's shoulders shook and Nicholas worried over her emotional state. Had she grown to care for her father? All at once, a giggle erupted and she buried her head in his chest to hide her laughter.

Nicholas didn't know if he could see him clearly, but he smiled for good measure. Mr. Brunon scowled as the boat sped up, leaving the small Polish town behind, along with the hope of finding his family.

LULA NESTLED DEEPER INTO NICHOLAS'S SIDE AS THE CITY OF Brusberg rose before them. The journey was short—a few hours at the most, but combined with the bitter wind of Christmas morning, it felt longer. Nicholas lifted her hand toward his face and kissed the ring on her finger. He couldn't think of a more precious Christmas gift.

"Welcome to Brusberg," he whispered.

Lula sat up from his embrace and squinted her eyes. "As long as it isn't Dalbeca."

Nervousness crept in at the thought of her expectations. "It's not fancy, Lula. Just a small farm and cottage."

Lula kissed his cheek and smiled. "It sounds perfect."

After docking the boat and paying Benson his due, Nicholas led the other three back toward Eulas's farm. It had been a long night and much needed rest awaited.

Minna bid farewell at the crossroad leading to the church, longing for her bed, but promised to visit the next day. They shuffled through the snow, shivering from head to toe as the roof of the barn appeared over the apple trees. Nicholas breathed in the cold air, the smell of hay and Franz ever-present.

It was comforting.

"Al, can you grab some extra firewood from the barn? We're going to need it tonight."

"Sure thing, Nic. Be back in a bit." Alius quickly shuffled, as fast as a man his height could go, to the stock pile of logs.

Nicholas grinned down at Lula.

She raised one brow. "You didn't need firewood, did you?"

He shrugged. "It doesn't hurt to have extra, but I really wanted to show you the cottage, you know, just us."

He opened the front door, but quickly spun and lifted

Lula in his arms, stepping over the threshold. He'd never seen her smile so bright—so content. He lightly kissed her lips before standing her upright.

Small, narrow beds sat on each side of the cabin, with the unbalanced, square table in the center. The one he ate dinner at every night with Eulas. The hearth of the fireplace took up one wall behind the door and a small counter with thick iron pots and wooden utensils crowded the opposite end of the cottage, beside the wood stove.

Nicholas kneeled to start a fire, then warmth and light blazed throughout the small space. "What do you think?" he asked.

Lula turned, thoughtfully, her gaze sliding over the old cabin she would now call home. "It's perfect."

"I know it's small, but we can get a bigger place when, well . . ." Nicholas fumbled over his words.

"When we have a family?" Lula blushed.

Nicholas fought a boyish smile, glanced down at the floor then back up. "Yeah. A family."

He absorbed the sight of her pink cheeks and the brown depths of her eyes that understood a hidden—unreachable part of himself. Even after all these years. Her pale, wind-blown locks hung across her shoulders and she took a small step forward. The air around the cottage became electric and amplified by their silence. Their eyes met and Nicholas struggled to take a breath. "Lula, I . . ."

At once, the front door burst open and Alius fumbled through the doorway with an armful of firewood. "Blimey, Nic. Grab a log, will ya?"

Nicholas exhaled, then reached to unload the chopped wood and add more to the flames. He stood to face Lula, nervous and unsure of himself. "Won't be long til sunrise. Maybe we should try to sleep."

Alius yawned, long and loud. "I agree."

Lula stood awkwardly staring at the two beds. Not three, two.

Nicholas hoped Alius would volunteer to catch a few hours of rest in the barn. He and Lula hadn't had a chance to process the events of the night and he would love to have a moment alone on their first night as husband and wife.

Alius stretched and scratched his belly as he shuffled toward the bed. "See you in a few," Alius mumbled around a yawn, then collapsed on the edge of the bed. He pulled the thick wool blanket around him, then paused at the tense expression on Nicholas's face. "What?" His forehead wrinkled in confusion.

Lula bit her top lip and avoided eye contact.

Alius's eyes widened in understanding. "Ah, Lu. I'm sorry. I didn't even think." He pushed the blanket away and struggled to sit up.

Nicholas exhaled in relief.

"You can sleep here, Lula. I'll sleep on the floor between you and Nicholas. I don't mind," Alius smiled as though proud of his thoughtfulness.

Lula's mouth fell open.

Nicholas cleared his throat. "You see, Al. We would like . . ."

"You can take the bed, Alius," Lula called out. "It's fine, I promise." She smiled brightly as Nicholas pursed his lips and stared at the ceiling.

"Oh, well, if you're sure, Lu." Alius snuggled deeper into the cozy bed and closed his eyes.

Nicholas and Lula turned toward each other, a mixture of amusement and disappointment hovering between them. Nicholas reached for Lula's hand, pulling her toward the other side of the room. He slipped off his boots, smirking up at her, then turned on his side underneath the covers and held his hand out for her to join him.

Lula fought a smile and shook her head, then laid on her side facing him. Nicholas held her tightly, brushing the loose strand of hair from her face and kissing her forehead.

"You won't be able to sleep comfortably," she whispered. "This bed is too small for you by yourself."

Nicholas chuckled. "It's never been warmer, though." He squeezed her tighter. "We'll get our sleeping arrangements sorted. I promise."

A loud, rumbling snore reverberated off the walls of the cottage followed by a high-pitch squeak of gas.

"Sooner rather than later, I hope," Lula mumbled.

18

LULA

*L*ula woke cold and alone to the sound of an over-exaggerated moan. She opened her eyes to the sight of a hairy belly mere feet from her bed. Alius stood, stretching his arms high over his head, shaking off the remnants of sleep.

"Mornin' Lu," he grumbled.

She closed her eyes and prayed for patience. "Good morning, Alius." She pushed her blonde tangles out of her face and squinted. "Where's Nicholas?"

"Bloake's probably been out for at least an hour now."

"An hour?" she asked.

Alius nodded. "Chores. Your husband is a hard-working farmer now." He laughed, cracking himself up.

Lula glanced away, struck by his words.

Husband.

Her gaze traveled around the small cabin—it wasn't much, but it was hers now. She had a responsibility as his wife. Lula scampered from the bed and Alius stared at her as if she'd lost her mind.

"Alright there, Lu? Spider in your bed? I can get it for

you." Alius stretched his short neck over the bed, searching for any sign of insects.

Lula tied her long hair in a knot over her head and gripped the sides of her boots, pushing her foot inside. "I have to get moving, Alius. Breakfast won't cook itself."

"Breakfast?" Alius's brows pulled together. "Haven't had a good breakfast in awhile. Do you need any help?"

Lula paused, glancing around, thoughtfully. "Could you gather some eggs while I light the wood stove?"

Alius took a step back, shaking his head. "Nope. I'm not going near that crazy chicken. Sorry Lu."

"Whatever are you rambling about?"

"That chicken wants to claw my eyes out, I tell you. She can't lay eggs anymore, but she thinks they are all hers. Nicholas hopes she'll kick the bucket soon. It's not worth your life, Lu. Believe me."

"Nonsense," Lula chuckled. "You've lost your mind."

Alius stood stone faced—he didn't think it was funny.

She sighed. "Can you gather some wood? I'll collect the eggs."

Alius shook his head as he opened the door. "Fine. But I'm telling Nicholas. He isn't going to like this." The door slammed behind him and Lula giggled at his absurdity. Crazy huhn. She rolled her eyes.

Lula sat in the corner of the barn, beside the chicken coop. The ragged brown feathers of the chicken in her lap frayed under her fingers as one blind, white eye focused on her face, as if glimpsing into her soul.

"Such a sweet girl, yes you are. You just need someone that understands you, that's all. We're going to be the best of friends." Lula snuggled the huhn closer and the chicken clucked, happily.

The barn door flung open as panicked voices filled the air. "Are you sure she said she was going to the barn? Maybe she's still in the house. Heidi would not appreciate a stranger coming toward her coop," Nicholas grumbled.

"I tried to tell her. Maybe we're too late. What if she's already dead?" Alius groaned. "How am I ever going to live with myself?"

Lula giggled. "I'm over here."

Nicholas rushed toward the coop and slid to a stop at the sight of his wife snuggling the mangy, sparse feathered huhn. "Are you crazy? That chicken is out for blood. Get away from her!"

Lula scoffed. "This huhn is the sweetest, most gentle animal I've ever held. You don't understand her, that's all."

"I understand she's vicious. And ugly. That's all I need to know."

Lula's mouth fell open. "Hush now."

The chicken clucked toward Nicholas as if supporting her newfound friend.

Nicholas glanced back and forth between his wife and the chicken that despised him. He shook his head in disbelief. "Fine. Have it your way. But don't say I didn't warn you." He turned away from the barn, mumbling along the way.

THROUGHOUT THE WEEK, LULA'S MOOD DARKENED. THE cottage had never been cleaner. Dinner was prepped and ready every evening and all of the animals had been fed twice a day. But she still hadn't spent five minutes alone with her husband. He had invited her for a stroll after lunch, to show her the surrounding land that bordered their property. Her belly clenched out of excitement as he gently took her hand in his and led her outside.

She craved time alone with him. The chance to hear about the years she'd missed and understand the man he had become. He had changed so much. Nicholas was tall and wide-shouldered with the same shaggy brown hair he had as a boy. His blue eyes were framed by thick lashes and sparkled when he laughed. He always kept his face shaved, and his sleeves rolled up. The years of labor had packed on muscle, but there was a softness that only Nicholas could pull off.

She wanted to know the man he had become.

Across the field, Alius ran as fast as his short legs would carry him while screaming, "Wait for me! I'm coming, too!"

Nicholas stopped, tilting his head back toward the sky. He sighed, loudly—then turned to meet Lula's eyes. "He doesn't get it, does he?"

Her cheeks expanded as she exhaled out of frustration. "You're going to have to talk to him."

"Talk to him?" His brows raised. "What would you like me to say?"

"Explain it to him. Tell him we haven't had a minute alone since we married and we need to . . ." Lula fumbled over her words.

Nicholas grinned. "Yes?"

"You know. We want time alone to . . ." A deep red blush crept along her pale cheeks.

"I'm listening." He crossed his arms in front of his chest and peered down at her.

Lula stomped her foot, embarrassed and irritated. "You can sleep with the pigs, Nicholas Klaus!" She spun, hurrying toward the cottage as he chuckled behind her.

As Alius reached her, he frowned at the apparent anger

radiating from her every step. He struggled to catch his breath. "Alright there, Lu?"

"You go ahead and keep him company. I have work to do."

"HELLO? ANYONE HERE?" A SHRILL VOICE CALLED OUT.

Lula stuck her head outside the barn door and smiled. "In here!"

Minna shuffled toward the barn, rambling along the way about the cold weather, the lack of discipline at the orphanage and the laziness of the staff. She looked to be in a mood similar to Lula's.

"Where are Nicholas and Alius?" Minna asked.

Lula shrugged. "Walking the property, I guess. I don't know." She glanced toward the ground where she had been spreading fresh hay.

"Everything okay?"

"Fine." Lula nodded, but refused to meet her eyes.

Minna mumbled to herself while plopping down in the hay, ungracefully. "I'm not. I've been managing the stalls on top of my regular duties at the orphanage and they don't seem to be interested in finding anyone to help. Why would they when I can do it all? You would think . . . Lula? Are you crying?"

Lula sniffed and shook her head. "No—I have something in my eye. That's all."

Minna narrowed her eyes. "Anyway, if they refuse to hire . . ."

Lula fell to her knees in tears. "How am I expected to be a proper wife? Tell me that!"

Minna jerked her head back, startled. "Well, um, I–"

"I cook. I clean. I take pride in my work, but that isn't all of my duties!" Lula widened her eyes at Minna. "You know what I mean?"

Minna opened her mouth then closed it again. She pursed her lips, then replied, "I guess so."

"When I wake up, he's the first one I see. Always offering to help. Sitting beside me at dinner. He's the last one I see before I go to bed. I can't take it anymore!" Lula screamed.

Minna scooted across the hay toward Lula. "There, there." She wrapped her arms around her friend and hugged tight, offering as much comfort as possible. "I think it will get easier—him being around all the time. Especially when you have kids, you'll appreciate his help. Just give it more time."

"Kids? He's going to be around when I have children?" Lula asked.

Minna chuckled. "Of course! He really is one of the most supportive men I know. He won't leave your side for a minute."

Lula buried her head in her hands and wailed louder. "I'll never have children because he won't go away."

Minna tilted her head as if confused. "Sorry?"

"He's always around, Minna! Alius won't leave."

Minna's mouth fell open in shock. "I thought you were talking about Nicholas. I'm sorry, Lula. I haven't even thought about Alius being here all the time."

Lula hiccuped. "It's not your fault. I feel inadequate, you know? I want to be a true wife to Nicholas. I hate to think he married me only to save me from marrying the general, like he doesn't want me the same way I do him."

"Hush, now. I'm sure that isn't true. You have to remember, Lula, Alius has only been here for a few weeks. Nicholas thought he'd drowned—he mourned for his friend. I imagine he feels terrible asking him to give you guys privacy."

Lula nodded. "You're probably right. I'm just emotional right now."

Minna hugged her once more then smiled. "Have room for one more tonight? I'll bring dessert."

Lula perked up and her eyes brightened. "I could use dessert."

LULA STIRRED VEGETABLE SOUP IN A LARGE IRON POT WHILE staring out the window in deep thought. Nicholas and Alius chatted behind her, about what, she didn't know. Her mind was elsewhere, still in the dark pit she'd climbed into earlier.

"Knock knock!" Minna called from the doorway, carrying her dessert.

Lula pasted a fake grin on her face and walked across the room to greet her. "This looks delicious."

"I hope so. It's rhubarb." Minna turned to grin at Alius, then attempted a shy curtsy, showing off her new cream-colored dress with a thick ruffled hem.

Alius tilted his head at her obvious effort, then wagged his eyebrows in her direction.

She giggled.

Lula glanced toward Nicholas and shook her head as he fought a smile. He then made the show of appreciating her outfit, wagging his brows in return. Lula snickered.

The four of them crowded around the small square table, digging into bowls of Lula's stew. The sound of crackling logs and Alius's slurping echoed along the walls of the tiny cottage.

Lula didn't have much of an appetite. She knotted her hands in her lap, thinking over the fears she admitted to Minna in the barn. What if Nicholas didn't want her as his wife? As selfless as he was, she could see him making the sacrifice of marrying someone he didn't love so that she would be free.

Minna sat up straight, clearing her throat. "Alius, I have wonderful news."

Alius lowered the near-empty bowl he had tilted against his lips. "Oh, yeah? What's that?"

"The orphanage has offered you a position in the stables."

He scoffed. "The stables? Why would I want to do that? Plus, Nic needs me here. Don't you?"

Nicholas's eyes widened, "Well, I mean, I don't want to hold you back. It's not like you couldn't visit all the time."

Alius opened his mouth to respond, but Minna cut him off. "You would be able to live in the service quarters with the rest of the staff. I thought it might be nice to have you closer, you know, to me." Minna batted her eyes.

Alius cleared his throat as a blush spread across his face.

Lula gripped Minna's hand underneath the table. She would never be able to repay her for this kindness.

Alius sat up straight and thrust his chest forward, as much as he could, anyway. "Well, if Nicholas is alright with it, I guess I can help out. At least for a bit."

"I think it's wonderful, Al." Nicholas responded.

"Oh, yes. You can walk me home tonight and I'll show you around. I do hate walking alone in the dark, you know."

The girl was good.

"Alright, Minna. That is, if Nicholas and Lula are sure."

"We're positive," Nicholas and Lula called out in unison.

After enjoying Minna's dessert, Nicholas walked with Alius and Minna to the door to bid goodbye. Lula stood behind him waving—promising to see them soon.

Nicholas turned in the doorway, peering down at her with dark eyes. He stepped forward and slammed the door behind him.

Lula took a step back, nervously. "I'll just, um, clean up."

She spun toward the large iron pot and gripped the hot handles with a towel. All at once, Nicholas's arms circled her from behind. His hands covered her own, forcing her to release her hold on the pot. Without a word, he turned her in his arms, and his amused eyes searched her own, but for what, she wasn't sure.

He took a step back—then another. Nicholas pulled her after him, grinning.

With one look, he erased the doubt that had stolen Lula's confidence in their marriage. With one touch, she felt more loved than ever before.

19

NICHOLAS

icholas walked along the orchards the following spring, inspecting the apple trees that had survived the brutal winter. He stopped at each tree, checking the bark for damage and fruit for disease—just as Eulas had taught him.

"Come now, Nicholas. Do we really have to stop at every tree?"

Nicholas grinned down at his impatient wife. "We have to keep our trees healthy or else we won't have enough for Christmas jam."

"Well, yes. But every apple?" She fought to contain her smile as he rolled his eyes.

"I need to be getting back anyway," he mumbled. "Alius is supposed to stop by. He said it was important."

"That sounds intriguing."

"Does it?" Nicholas grinned. "The last time he needed to chat, it was about a rash on his . . ."

"You don't need to tell me, really. As intriguing as Alius can be," she fought a smile and lowered her eyes toward the ground. "I wanted to talk to you about something."

He knew that look. "Yes? Go on."

"Berta has been on my mind lately. I feel guilty leaving the way we did."

Nicholas stopped and turned toward Lula. He'd felt quite a bit of guilt over the years for the way they had left. They never considered how much it would hurt her. At that age—they only knew they wanted more out of life. They struggled to comprehend the feelings of the woman who had watched over them for years.

"I agree. Maybe we should reach out and let her know we're alright."

Lula grinned, then nodded. "Also, I would like to find out how many children are there now. We always said we would bring Christmas back to the orphans. So why don't we? We could send them Christmas gifts."

Nicholas's thumb grazed her cheek and he smiled at the thought. "I've been thinking of reaching out to several churches and orphanages—to see if they wanted to adopt our Christmas Eve tradition. The more people we can help, the better."

The smile that spread across Lula's face could brighten the darkest day. "That sounds lovely."

Nicholas shoveled manure from Franz's pen into the wagon, grateful for the fertilizer—the potato fields would need it. The pig squealed and snorted in his direction like he always did. Franz would much prefer the company of Lula—as did all of the animals.

He couldn't blame them. His wife was not only kind, but gentle. Nicholas glanced up at Lula, knee deep in her flower gardens out front. He couldn't wait to see her as a mother one day.

He heard Alius's heavy breathing before he saw him. His short legs hurried toward the barn as he gripped a wooden crate in his stubby arms.

"Another load already? How do you do it?" Nicholas asked.

"We barely had enough toys last Christmas, Nic. I want plenty to go around, you know."

Nicholas took the crate of toys and peered inside. "What's this?"

"Oh, Minna has discovered a love for sewing. She's making cloth dolls for the girls."

"That's brilliant. Tell her I said thanks."

"Will do." Alius shuffled his feet along the dirt, nervously. "I'd like to talk to you about something."

"Alright, but if it's like last time, I don't want to see it."

"What? Oh, no it's not anything like that." Alius cleared his throat and took a deep breath. He opened his mouth, then shut it. Then, he opened it again. "It's like jam."

"Jam?" Nicholas tilted his head to the side.

Alius nodded. "I never liked jam. It wasn't worth the work I put into it, you know?"

"Are you saying you don't want to make jam this year for Christmas?"

"What? No." Alius shook his head, annoyed. "I'm saying that maybe I didn't like it because it wasn't worth the trouble. But what if a sweet fruit came along that is worth it?"

Nicholas scratched the back of his head as he stared at the ground. "Are you saying you would rather have pear jam?"

"Blimey, Nic. This has nothing to do with jam!"

Nicholas threw his hands into the air and raised his voice. "Then why are we talking about it?"

"How do you not understand? It isn't difficult!" Alius's face turned red and he took a deep breath. "Let's try this a different way. You love apple jam, right?"

Nicholas nodded, impatiently.

"And you hate blackberry jam, right?"

"Well, yes. The seeds get stuck in my teeth," Nicholas replied.

Alius nodded. "So it isn't worth it for you to put in the work for blackberry jam, right?"

"I guess not." Nicholas shrugged.

"Exactly!" Alius smiled brightly as if everything made sense. "That is how I feel!"

"But I thought you liked blackberry jam," Nicholas yelled, annoyed.

Alius threw his hands into the air and started pacing alongside Baret's fence.

"Hi, Alius. How's it going?" Lula stared between the two men and her eyes widened as if she'd interrupted. "I can leave . . ."

"No, it's fine, Lula." Alius plastered a fake smile on his frustrated face. "I was trying to explain to Nicholas that sometimes people don't think they like jam, but then learn that they do."

Lula threw her hands over her face and squealed in excitement. She jumped toward Alius, wrapping her arms around his neck. "You're asking Minna to marry you?"

Nicholas threw his hands in the air the same way Alius had seconds earlier. "What? What are you talking about?"

Alius grinned sheepishly at Lula. "Do you think she'll say yes? The orphanage has offered me a permanent position and housing to run their stables."

"You're proposing?" Nicholas shouted.

"Of course she'll say yes!" Lula and Alius embraced once again as Nicholas watched—baffled.

"Can someone please tell me what's going on?"

"For heaven's sake, Nicholas." She grinned. "Alius has found his favorite jam."

Nicholas and Lula stood proud as the bride and groom made their way to their cottage. Their intimate group, along with Father Gorski and the orphans that Minna had grown close to, clapped and cheered as Alius fought to lift his lanky wife. Her long legs dangled as he continued to lose his balance—shifting from side to side. But Alius was determined to carry her over the threshold. After making it across, he shouted a very enthusiastic yelp and slammed the door. The crowd chuckled as everyone clapped for the newlyweds.

Alius deserved this little bit of happiness he'd found with Minna. He needed to be loved, cherished, and stared at the way she did him. As if he were her everything. Nicholas stared down at Lula—his everything.

Father Gorski clapped Nicholas on the back. "Thank you for this. Being able to marry Alius and Minna means more than you know. I don't think I could've gotten to Brusberg without you. Money is—tight." He grimaced as if hating to admit it.

"Proud to give back," Nicholas told him. "We have reserves from the market, I'd like to help if you'll let me."

"You've done enough." Father Gorski looked toward Lula. "I know this isn't the best time, but . . ."

"What is it?" Lula frowned.

"I need to speak with you before I leave for Dalbeca." Father Gorski nodded toward the side of the church as everyone continued to clean up the remaining flowers and ribbons. They followed him to an isolated corner and Nicholas's stomach dropped at the look of worry on his face.

"I'm sorry, but your father . . ." He cleared his throat. "Mr. Brunon has passed."

Nicholas stared down at his wife, concerned. He knew

she didn't think of him as her father, but they couldn't change the fact that he was. Being an orphan, you spend your life desperate to know where you came from. How would this affect her?

Lula froze, as if she didn't know how to feel.

"I'm not asking you to say or do anything, but I felt as though you should know," Father Gorski continued. "His property is being sold to pay his debts."

"Debts?" Lula questioned. As she waited for an explanation, her eyes darkened in understanding. "Like a dowry?"

Father Gorski didn't respond.

She looked down at her wringing hands and exhaled. "How—how did he die?"

He looked away as if uncomfortable. "It's, well, it's unknown at this point. He was found at the bottom of the stairs."

Lula's balance faltered and Nicholas stepped closer, wrapping his arm around her. "I know what you're thinking," he whispered. "This wasn't your fault."

Father Gorski nodded. "He's right, Lula. Even if there was foul play, Mr. Brunon's choices were his own."

She swallowed and took a minute to process his words."So there's nothing I need to do?" she asked.

He shook his head. "Not unless you want to."

"I don't." Lula's bottom lip quivered. "It's over?" Tears filled her eyes as her gaze landed on the priest.

"It's over. That part of your life is done."

NICHOLAS SHUFFLED THROUGH THE OVERGROWN FIELD, shielding his eyes from the sun, as the chirping of frogs surrounded him. The birch tree rose in the distance, and he swallowed the familiar lump in his throat. It never failed—

just the sight of Eulas's favorite tree brought a fresh wave of grief.

He sat, elbows resting on bent knees. Nicholas closed his eyes and breathed in and out, needing to feel just a glimpse of his presence—an inkling of his spirit.

"You told me to never be ashamed to show my feelings. So forgive me if I struggle to hold it together." He paused to gather his thoughts. "You left me too soon. There was so much I needed to learn from you."

His nose burned and his throat squeezed tight. "Some days, I think I can actually do this—take your place. I manage the farm, market sales are enough to live on, and Lula seems content. But for some reason, something keeps telling me this is a stop along the way. It doesn't make sense."

Nicholas's voice cracked as he whispered, "I don't know what to do. I'm married and we want to start a family. How can I be so determined to take care of the rest of the world when I have my own house to tend to? Help me. Tell me what to do. I'm struggling to fight it—the drive to contribute to the lives of others. Just like you did for me."

All at once, the birds and frogs quieted and silence consumed the field. A cool breeze suddenly whipped around his face as if caressing him. He grinned as a single tear rolled down his cheek. "I love you, too."

20

NICHOLAS

*O*n a hot summer day, Lula and Minna sat in rocking chairs, while Nicholas and Alius relaxed on the porch beside them. The last couple of years were spent exactly like this, in the company of close friends. Everyday, after chores were completed, Nicholas and Lula walked together around the property, respectfully stopping at Eulas's favorite birch tree, and eating a picnic lunch in the afternoon. During the evenings, Alius and Minna would visit.

Minna breathed heavily, suffering through the summer heat while her hand traveled over her large round belly out of habit. Nicholas watched as his wife's eyes traveled over her pregnant friend in longing.

"How much longer, Minna?" Lula asked.

"Too long. I have three months to go and I look as though I could pop at any moment. You know what Mr. Pendergrass at the General Store asked me? He asked if I was overdue. He said his wife never gained this much weight. Can you believe that?"

"Blimey, Minna. I'll give him a what for—you just say the

word." Alius's chest blew up at the thought of someone disrespecting his wife.

"It's fine. His wife told me not to pay him any mind." Minna leaned forward as if Mr. Pendergrass could hear her. "She said he's a smidgen sly of a loaf, if you know what I mean."

"Well, I think you look lovely," Lula interjected. "Glowing even."

"Nah," Minna mumbled. "That's just the sweat."

"Ladies, I hate to break up the party, but I have some work to do." Nicholas stood, dusting off his pants, then brushed Lula's cheek in passing.

Lula grinned toward Minna. "Come inside. I have some pie with your name on it."

Minna scampered out of the rocking chair faster than Nicholas thought possible.

"Need some help, Nic?" Alius didn't wait on his answer as he stumbled from the porch, chasing after him.

Nicholas peeked over his shoulder and laughed. "Tryin' to run away from your bride?"

Alius grumbled. "She's a beast I tell you. Blames me for everything. Don't have a baby with Lula. I'm warning you—it changes them."

"Al, the poor woman has to be miserable. Give her a break." Nicholas stopped walking and met Alius's eyes. "Besides, I'm not sure if we can have children, Alius."

Alius's face fell. "I'm sorry, Nic. Didn't think of that when I opened my big mouth. Minna said Lula had been in a horrible state about it."

Nicholas nodded. "She wants a child. She's always dreamed of a family of her own." His heart squeezed painfully at not being able to give her everything she always wanted. She deserved it. Lula deserved the world.

"Don't give up. Never know what's in store. Right?"

Nicholas and Alius continued toward the barn. "That's right, Al. You never know what will happen."

Nicholas and Alius worked on replacing the weathered planks on the back side of the barn. Well, Nicholas worked while Alius supervised, telling him where to hammer his nails to gain the most support.

Around the time the last plank went up, a scratchy and nervous sounding voice called out from behind them. "Alius?"

Alius and Nicholas spun toward the unfamiliar woman and froze. They needed no introduction—it was obvious by the short stature and wavy orange hair, sticking up in all directions. Her eyes held disbelief, and she wrung her hands in front of her plump belly as if anxious.

"Ma? Ma, is that you?"

Alius took a small step forward and stopped, as if he couldn't believe his eyes. His mother held her arms out in invitation, but was unable to reply. Tears filled her large brown eyes and her head shook as if in shock. Alius stepped forward again—slowly. He stopped within inches of her face and his gaze traveled over every feature.

Alius's eyes met hers, then he fell to his knees, clinging to her skirts as he cried tears of joy. His mother wrapped her arms around his head and held tight. She leaned back as if to get a better look at him, then brushed his hair from his face.

"Argos . . . I'm so sorry about Argos," Alius cried.

"You're alive. That's what matters now."

Nicholas couldn't believe his eyes. How did she get here? After all these years, Alius had been reunited with his family. Nicholas didn't know what to do. Should he invite her inside? Give them privacy?

After a few minutes, he stepped forward. "Ma'am?"

Her eyes never left her son as she spoke. "You must be Nicholas. I've heard all about you from Father Gorski." She grinned a toothy, happy smile while staring at Alius. "I'm Golden Evett, but you can call me Goldie."

Alius pulled back, his face covered in tears and sweat. "How? How did you find me?"

"Got your letter we did! Your Aunt Aly received it and passed it along to us. You can't imagine how thrilled we were when we heard you were alive. We thought for sure you'd passed alongside Argos." She cupped the sides of his face. "My sweet boy."

"Aunt Aly? So that's where you've been? In Scotland?"

"That's right. The whole family moved there after we thought we lost you. Your father, Gary, Tina, Sharon, Ronnie, Lybron and all of their kids. All except Todd and Marie—you know they joined that circus in town. The one with the two-headed dog?" She leaned in to whisper, "They never were quite right." Goldie shook her head and focused. "Anyway, I've been searching since forever. I finally made my way to Dalbeca and almost lost hope until I happened upon Father Gorski."

Goldie's expression softened. "He told me everything, Alius. Owe him for taking care of my boy."

"We were lucky, Ma. Nicholas and I both were lucky to find help along the way. I'm so happy to see you." Alius grinned and Nicholas could see the love in his eyes for his mother.

Goldie clapped her hands, enthusiastically. "And I hear I have a daughter-in-law! Where is she? I have to meet her!"

"Alius? What's going on?"

He spun toward the back door of the barn where Minna held her belly with one hand and leaned up against the frame with the other. Alius shuffled toward his wife and stood by her side with pride.

"Ma? I'd like you to meet my wife, Minna." He grinned, waiting.

Goldie looked her over from head to toe and her mouth fell open. "Sweet baby Jesus, Alius. What have you done to her? You shouldn't be on your feet in your last month!"

Alius shook his head toward his mother—hinting for her to bite her tongue. Minna gasped and her eyes filled with tears. "I have three months left!"

Goldie cut her eyes toward Alius as if trying to determine if they were pulling her leg. She quickly pasted on a fake, uncomfortable smile. "No matter, dear. Ma is here now and everything will be alright. Your mother-in-law is the best midwife around."

Minna glanced toward Alius, panicked. He stood frozen, unsure what to say.

Nicholas's voice came out higher than he intended, "Why don't we all go inside and talk. We have so much to catch up on." His bright smile did little to defuse the tension, but Goldie didn't seem affected in the least. She appeared giddy as she followed Alius and Minna toward the house.

All at once, Goldie looked over her shoulder at Nicholas and her steps faltered. Nicholas reached out to catch her, but she wasn't concerned about the loss of balance. Her eyes met his and she tilted her head. It was the first time she truly paid attention to him since she had arrived.

"You . . . You were in the orphanage with Alius?"

"Yes, Ma'am." He nodded, then looked past her toward Alius.

"For how long?"

"An infant. A fisherman found me on the shore late one night in Dalbeca. I'm afraid I can't tell you more than that."

Goldie nodded her head. "Yes. It was late—and stormy, twenty years ago. I'll never forget the howling of the wind against the windows. The crack of thunder overhead—we were terrified."

Nicholas searched her eyes for answers. "How do you

know that?" He gripped her upper arms tight. "How do you know me?"

"I was there the night you were born."

Lula sat a tray of tea and pastries on the small table inside the cottage—everyone took a seat either in the wooden dining chairs or on the side of Nicholas and Lula's bed.

Nervous silence filled the air as Nicholas waited. Waited to hear the words he'd yearned for since he was a child. Where did he come from? Where were his parents?

"You look just like him, you know. Your father. Especially the eyes—that's how I knew it was you."

Nicholas didn't respond, but sat staring at her while rubbing his thumb back and forth across his chin. Lula leaned into him, as if offering comfort.

"Your mother, Miriam Starosta, was a dear friend of mine. Raised by her father, who's love for exploring kept him from home. He had a vision—wanted to change the world, he did. But it was a lonely life for Miriam. Unfortunately she fell in love with the wrong man, a fellow by the last name of Kasak.

After a back injury at work, he became addicted to laudanum. He was unreliable and she barely had enough to survive on. He wasn't there the night Miriam gave birth and that was the final straw. She was already weak and too thin— but then we couldn't stop the bleeding and there was nothing we could do." Goldie teared up at the memory and her eyes begged Nicholas to forgive her.

"She made me promise to take you to the church—hide you away so you could never be tainted by his ugliness. We offered to take you as our own, but she knew it wouldn't work. Your father would expect something like that. So, my husband, Kev, took you to St. Mary's, just like your mother asked. We told your father you died during childbirth, alongside her."

Lula's grip on Nicholas's arm tightened. No one knew what to say.

Nicholas glanced down at his feet, processing her words. "So my mother is dead?"

Goldie nodded and her chin trembled. "I'm so sorry, Nicholas. We never knew what happened to you after that, but that was the way she wanted it. She never wanted a trail leading him back to you."

Nicholas nodded, but still refused to meet her eyes. "And my father? Do you know what happened to him?"

"I imagine he's still alive, as stubborn as the man was. After Miriam died, his family refused to have him—ashamed of him. Probably riding the train as he did for years after her death.

"The train?" Nicholas asked.

Goldie nodded. "That's right. From what I understand, Tomek never left that train again."

"Tomek?" Alius asked. "Why do I know that name?"

Nicholas stood and paced the room as tension and disbelief flooded the small cottage.

Lula was the first to speak. "Tomek was the first person we met on the train after running away from the orphanage." Her eyes bored into Nicholas's back as he stared out the window. "I can see it now," Lula whispered. "You have the same eyes."

Nicholas shook all over. Tomek was his father? How could that be? He recalled their conversation that night on the train—the guilt Tomek felt over the mistakes in his life. Nicholas turned toward the crowded cottage. He knew they were waiting for him to react.

"I . . . I need to go for a walk."

He spun toward the door and slammed it behind him. There was only one person he yearned to talk to, even though they would never answer back. In the distance, the top of the old birch tree swayed as if greeting an old friend.

21

NICHOLAS

The smell of ammonia and urine filled the air as Nicholas covered his nose with a handkerchief. Father Gorski stood close, just as he had the past couple of weeks. As much as he missed his wife and best friend, he was thankful the priest was here instead—he wasn't sure what he would find or how it would affect him emotionally.

As soon as Nicholas decided to search for Tomek, Father Gorski insisted on going. It wasn't an easy decision, and one that was made late one night under the moonlight beside the old birch tree. Whether it was guidance from Eulas, or what Nicholas knew he would say, something whispered he would regret it if he didn't try.

Lula and Alius remained in Brusberg to take care of the farm and stay close to Minna. Nicholas hadn't planned on being gone longer than a week, but they ran into a dead end when Tomek was nowhere to be found. Nicholas searched every train that he came across—moving or unmoving. The forests and surrounding hills showed no sign of him.

Right when they believed all hope was lost, a railroad worker recognized their description and pointed them to the

Dalbeca Infirmary. He'd found Tomek unconscious a couple of weeks before, burning up with fever. Around the same time Goldie told Nicholas the truth about his parents.

Timing is everything.

Nicholas and Father Gorski slowly shuffled down the bare and desolate hallway of the infirmary—echoes of sick men and women coughing the only sound. The room was dark, barely lit by lanterns on the wall as Nicholas's gaze searched every bed down the aisle, searching for his father.

His heart squeezed painfully at the thought of being too late.

A petite, young nurse dressed in white stood at the foot of a bed, paper chart in hand. Her dark hair was pulled tight in a neat bun, but the bags under her eyes showed exhaustion and lack of sleep.

"Excuse me? Can you tell me where I can find Tomek Kasak?"

She responded without glancing up from her chart. "Are you a relative?"

Nicholas faltered. He swallowed the lump in his throat and then whispered, "I'm his son."

The nurse closed the chart and looked up with a smile. "He's down the hall, four beds to the right. He's been quite agreeable, as long as you don't take his blanket." She grinned before turning away.

"Sorry? His blanket?"

Glancing over her shoulder, she said, "He came in with it —said it was a gift."

He nodded, unable to speak.

Nicholas made his way forward until the familiar blanket came into view. The same one that Berta used to tuck around him at the orphanage. Eight years. Tomek had clung to an eight-year-old wool blanket because he didn't have anything else.

He didn't have anyone.

Father Gorski gripped his shoulder in support as he watched the sleeping man before him. He was frail and unhealthy looking. Tomek's wiry beard was longer than he remembered and the wrinkles around his eyes more pronounced, but otherwise he looked the same.

Nicholas didn't know what he expected to feel. If anything, he thought he would be angry. He would demand to know what could be more important than taking care of your wife and child. But he felt only pity.

Eulas's words whispered through his mind as if he stood there beside him. "I can't think of anything more powerful than showing grace to someone who's done nothing to deserve it."

Tomek groaned as if in pain, then raised his head to cough. He blinked, disoriented, then relaxed against his pillow, staring up at his visitors with confusion.

"You—" He pointed toward Nicholas. "I know you."

Nicholas pulled a small stool forward to sit down. "I know you, too."

"Did you come back for your blanket?" Tomek's chuckle turned into a gasp, then a nasty wet cough. "I won't give it up without a fight, you know. It's saved my life over the years." He gripped the blanket tight against his chest and Nicholas knew he wasn't referring to it's warmth.

"I think you need it more than I do," Nicholas whispered.

Tomek's grip relaxed and he inhaled through his nose. "What are you doing here?"

Nicholas sighed. "It seems we have something in common, Tomek."

Tomek stared, but didn't reply.

"Miriam Starosta." Nicholas's voice broke, unable to say more.

Tomek's eyes widened, and he licked across dry lips

before responding. "I don't know what you're talking about." He turned his head to the side as a tear ran down his cheek.

Nicholas knew there was no easy way to say this. "I'm your son, Tomek."

Tomek's frail shoulders shook as he fought his emotions. He closed his eyes as if everyone would disappear, like it was all a dream.

Nicholas continued, "I don't want anything from you. I know you were told I didn't survive. Honestly, I don't know why I'm here. I guess I wanted to tell you—I forgive you."

Tomek's surprised gaze met his. "Forgive me? You don't know what you're talking about." He held his stomach as another wave of coughs took control of his body. He winced from the pain before speaking once again.

"Miriam was an angel. The only thing in my life worth having. I lost sight of our future and she paid the price. Along with you. I'm not worthy of forgiving. I'm not worth anything." Tomek closed his eyes as if the struggle to speak took everything he had. "I'm getting exactly what I deserve."

Nicholas looked back toward Father Gorski and remembered something he once said. "Tomek, someone once told me that we are only human and not expected to be perfect. That's why God forgives."

Tomek's nose flared and he struggled to swallow. Nicholas could tell the words surprised him. He whispered, "You think he'd forgive someone like me?"

Nicholas turned toward Father Gorski and nodded. The priest took his place on the stool and listened to every word as Tomek confessed his sins and asked God to forgive him. Father Gorski pulled a small vial from his satchel and rubbed the oil across Tomek's forehead, whispering, "May the Lord who frees you from sin save you and raise you up."

Tomek's gaze met Nicholas's as he fought to keep his eyes open. He reached out in invitation and Nicholas stepped around the other side of the bed to grip his hand. Tomek gasped as speaking became difficult.

"I don't deserve this. But I need to ask you to do something for me."

Nicholas nodded.

"Be the man I couldn't."

As Tomek took his last breath, one hand clinging to Father Gorski and the other to his own son, the heaviness in his eyes dissipated into peace as he let go of the horrors in his life. He was free, and Nicholas was grateful for the chance to say goodbye—the opportunity to forgive. Not everyone was so lucky.

The hot humid air stuck to Nicholas's skin as he waited outside the infirmary for Father Gorski. Nicholas wasn't sure what life had in store, but he would continue to take care of his family and pray for guidance. The spirit of Eulas would live on in Brusberg and everywhere else Nicholas could reach. But first, there was something he needed to do.

He struggled to understand the road Tomek had taken— or if he even had a choice. He spent the best years of his life wallowing in a puddle of guilt and sadness for what he had lost—for the pain he had created.

"Alright there, Son?"

Nicholas nodded toward Father Gorski. "Thanks for coming with me tonight."

"Watching a man humble himself before God is an honor, Nicholas. Thank you for letting me be a part of it."

Nicholas didn't know what to say. The events of the night had emotionally drained him, and he sat in the silent streets outside the infirmary, struggling to wrap his mind around everything.

"I've arranged for him to be buried here in Dalbeca." Nicholas spoke as if convincing himself he'd done the right thing. Nothing about this felt right.

"Why don't you come back with me and get some rest. You can head back to Brusberg in the morning," the priest offered.

Nicholas turned to face him, his brows pulled together in thought. "Thanks for the offer, but I have something I want to do before I go."

"Do you need me to come along?"

Nicholas shook his head, "No. I need to do this myself. But thank you again. You're always there when I need you."

Father Gorski stepped onto the street, then grinned up at Nicholas. "Of course. That's what family is for." Then he walked down the cobblestone path that would lead to his cottage.

Nicholas turned, walking in the opposite direction. He traveled for several hours, down the worn path to the river—then the woods leading to the train tracks. He remembered every turn like it was yesterday. Nicholas strode along the train tracks for a little while longer until the sound of a whistle sounded near. He waited for the perfect time and jumped into an open car toward Torek.

He was exhausted—emotionally and physically. He propped himself up in the corner of the car and closed his eyes, the rumble of the train track lulling him to sleep.

"You're too big to be an orphan," the small girl shouted. "I think you're fibbing!" Dark brown pig-tails swung from side to side as her eyes narrowed in disbelief.

"Well," Nicholas said. "I was an orphan. I'm not necessarily an orphan now."

After Nicholas arrived in Torek, he walked straight to the orphanage. The only home he knew as a child. Intending to speak with Berta, he headed to the front door, but halted when a group of orphans caught his attention under the same tree he used to play under as a boy.

His feet were moving toward the playground before his mind could catch up. It wasn't the little girl braiding another's hair or the tall boy with a ripped boot climbing the tree. It was the small child in the corner—observant, but alone. He collected twigs and rocks of equal size and lined them perfectly in front of him, reaching forward every now and again to ensure preciseness.

The orphans avoided him, acting as though he wasn't even there. The child was obviously different and not easily accepted by the others. Something about the boy pulled at Nicholas's heart.

He wanted to talk to him, understand what was going through his head. A spunky child with pigtails and freckles immediately stepped in front of him, asking questions faster than he could answer. Somehow, he found himself sitting in the center of a group of children, explaining how he used to live there, but moved to Brusberg. They asked question after question.

"How old are you?"

Nicholas responded, "I'm—"

"Are you homeless?"

"What?" Nicholas asked.

The little girl with pigtails raised her voice. "I bet you don't even have a girlfriend."

He smiled. "Actually, I have a—"

"Don't you think you need a haircut? That's probably why you don't have a girlfriend."

Nicholas gave up answering their questions and pointed

toward the small boy, sitting all alone. "Who's that over there?"

"We don't know his name. He doesn't talk."

Nicholas watched him with narrowed eyes. "Maybe he's shy."

"Barry and Michael say he isn't very bright."

Nicholas opened his mouth in shock. "That's not very—"

"Who are you? What are you doing on church property?" A shriek voice called out.

Although deeper than he remembered, he would know that voice anywhere.

Nicholas stood and slowly turned toward Berta. The creases around her eyes had deepened over the years and wisps of thin gray hair blew across her face. Her angry gaze narrowed behind thick glasses, then widened in shock. Her hand splayed across her chest as she stepped closer.

"Nicholas? Is that you?"

"It's me, Berta." Nicholas gave a half smile and shrugged.

Tears filled her eyes as she sniffed, struggling to control her emotions and compose herself. She stood up straight and brushed her hands down her dress. "Well . . . thank heavens. I feared the worst over the years."

Nicholas walked forward, towering over her. He wrapped his arms around Berta until her body relaxed under his and embraced him in return.

"Welcome home," she whispered.

"So you finally married the girl? It's about time." Berta mumbled from across the table.

Nicholas smiled over the plate of red cabbage. "Was there ever any doubt?"

She chuckled and shook her head. "I'm so happy you're all

safe and sound. I can't tell you what this visit has done for my heart, Nicholas."

He stopped chewing—absorbing the truth of her words. "We never meant to hurt you, Berta. We were young and careless."

Berta leaned forward and tilted her head to the side, like she used to do when she demanded our attention. "You listen here. You might have been young, but you've never been careless, not with the feelings of others. You did what you thought was right. I can't fault you for that."

Berta leaned back and sighed. "You've always been different, Nicholas. Unique. I'm not going to pretend to understand it." She shook her head and grinned. "I'm just thankful to have a small part in what you'll accomplish one day."

Nicholas struggled to swallow, feeling both overwhelmed and undeserving of her praise. "I'm just an orphan from Torek."

"Hmph," she grunted. "Orphan or not. Mark my words— you're gonna change the world."

Nicholas smiled at her enthusiasm, then the small boy, alone in the corner, caught his attention once again. He stirred the kasza in his bowl, three stirs then a bite. The boy repeated it over and over. "What's the story?" Nicholas nodded over Berta's shoulder.

She turned, then looked back at Nicholas with sad eyes. "Marek? I know very little, I'm afraid. His father dropped him off, saying he was worthless. He hasn't spoken since he arrived."

"Can he talk?"

Berta shrugged. "I haven't gotten a word out of him." She tilted her head and smiled. "Would you like to try?"

Nicholas watched the child. How he hesitantly lifted the spoon toward his mouth, glancing around the dining hall as if self-conscious. His brown eyes met Nicholas's for several seconds before he lowered his gaze.

He walked across the dining hall and stood before the small boy. The orphan refused to look up and Nicholas could swear his hands were shaking.

"Can I sit down?"

Silence.

The last thing he wanted was to scare the child, and he almost turned away.

Almost.

As he stepped back, the boy peeked up and Nicholas faltered when he recognized something unexpected, yet familiar, in his eyes. Hope. A hope that he knew all too well.

A hope that someone cared.

A hope that someone understood.

Nicholas sat across from him and smiled. "I'm Nicholas. I was an orphan here just like you once. Berta is a respectable lady—she'll take care of you. She cares about her children."

The boy cleared his throat, but didn't respond. His gaze danced around the room as if he struggled to keep eye contact.

"Do you have a name?"

Silence.

"Well, that's alright. I gotta call you something, though. How about Borys?"

The child jerked his head back as if insulted, then shook his head.

"No? Okay, then. Oskar?"

He slumped and frowned.

"Tymon?"

Nicholas laughed at the scowl on his freckled face. "You'll have to help me out, you know."

Silence.

Nicholas sighed. "It's hard making friends, isn't it? For

some it's easy. As if they were born to be loved and adored. I was lucky because I found two great friends and they are my family now. That's what orphans have to do—make our own family. It isn't something we were given like everyone else. Do you understand?"

The boy's chin trembled as he shook his head. He didn't understand. Not at all.

"We have to make our own life, little man. Our own path. You have to decide who you want to be. You have to start right now."

The child's eyes widened as if the light flickered in understanding.

Nicholas grinned. "Now. Who do you want to be?"

The boy swallowed, then pointed a shaky finger toward Nicholas.

Nicholas sat back, surprised. "Me? You want to be me?"

He grinned and nodded.

Nicholas was taken aback. "You'll be a far greater man than me one day. I just know it."

Nicholas leaned forward. "Did I hear your name is Marek?"

Marek's smile grew wider and he sat up proud.

"It's nice to meet you, Marek."

Marek nodded, then continued pushing cabbage around the plate, humming the familiar tune of 'Holy God, We Praise Thy Name.'

Nicholas's breath caught in his throat and his chest ached. Memories of Eulas's deep voice flooded his mind. "Where did you hear that?" he pressed. "That song?"

Marek froze, then shook his head as if confused.

All at once, Nicholas closed his eyes as warmth embraced him, then it vanished as quick as it appeared.

He looked over at Marek and smiled. "I've always loved that hymn."

22

NICHOLAS

*L*ula danced from one side of the cottage to the other, oblivious to Nicholas's presence. He arrived home from Torek hours before, but hadn't made it inside. He wanted to watch her a little longer from the orchards, absorbing the beauty of her light.

Her pale hair swung free as she skipped around in a modest nightgown, cleaning an already spotless home. She sang a tune he couldn't hear, but it didn't matter. Lula was his song. She always would be.

Nicholas thought back to Berta's words and he fought to drown out the voice pushing him to do more. Feed more. Save more. The words angered him as he stood to his feet and dusted the grass from his trousers.

"I'm only one man," he grumbled. He glanced down into the most confused brown eyes he'd ever seen. "Sorry, Marek. Just talking to myself."

Fear overwhelmed his gratefulness of having Marek by his side. Nicholas was afraid Lula would be mad at him for making such a big decision without her. He was worried she would think he had lost hope of having their own child, and decided to adopt.

That wasn't it. The child was lost. Marek had no idea who he was and no one knew that feeling more than Nicholas. He knew exactly what the boy was thinking, even though he never spoke. They were connected on a level others couldn't understand.

He eased the wooden door open, as Lula danced and sang in a world of her own. Leaning against the door frame, he crossed his arms in front of his chest and smirked. His eyes widened as the sleeve of her long white nightgown slid down one shoulder.

He cleared his throat and she froze, spinning toward the doorway. Her mouth fell open as she pulled the fallen sleeve in place and blushed.

"You're home," she whispered.

He grinned. "I'm home."

Lula ran forward, but froze at the sight of the boy clinging to Nicholas's coat. Her eyes traveled to her husband and he smiled sadly.

"I went to see Berta," Nicholas whispered.

Lula inhaled, processing his words. She peeked around Nicholas to get a better view of the child. "I see."

Nicholas stepped closer and spoke under his breath. "Look, I know it's a lot. I don't know what I was thinking. He was just so . . . lost. There was a connection, you know?"

Lula stared into his eyes, as if trying to wrap her mind around the surprise. She took a deep breath, stepped around Nicholas and kneeled down in front of the child.

"I'm Lula. What's your name?"

The boy's chin quivered and he refused to meet her gaze.

"He, um, doesn't speak." Nicholas called out. "His name is Marek."

Lula looked over her shoulder toward Nicholas and

sympathy filled her eyes. She turned toward the child with a smile. "Well, Marek. Talking is overrated. There's something about the quiet, isn't there? It brings peace to the mind."

Marek's eyes traveled around the small cottage and he nodded. Lula reached forward to brush the hair from his brow and he flinched. Her eyes narrowed, but Nicholas wasn't sure if it was in anger at what he had been through or sorrow for his past.

Lula's voice softened. "Marek? We will never hurt you. Do you understand?"

He nodded, just enough for them to know he heard.

"Good. Would you like some pie?"

The child didn't respond, but searched over Lula's shoulder, curiously.

Lula led him to the table, placing a slice of pie and milk in front of him, then stepped out onto the porch with Nicholas.

As soon as the door shut, Nicholas blurted, "I'm so sorry, Lula, really. He refused to look at anyone and Berta said he was getting pushed by the others. The orphanage is at capacity and farmers are adopting children as farm-hands just to have free labor. That's not family. I couldn't ignore this feeling that if anyone understood, if anyone could change this child's life, it would be . . ."

"Us?" she asked, tearfully.

Nicholas rambled out of nervousness. "We always said we would adopt one day, especially after growing up in an orphanage. Berta said I should speak with you before taking in a child, but I couldn't imagine you refusing him. Plus, what if someone else came along in the meantime to adopt Marek? Someone who didn't understand him. "

"Nicholas, it's okay," she whispered. "I was just surprised, that's all."

"So you're not angry?"

She palmed the side of his face and smiled. "I love you,

you know that? Things like this is why I fell for you in the first place. I think you knew I would have done the same thing."

Nicholas stood up straight, feeling safe enough to stop groveling. "Yeah, you would have." He pulled her against his chest and greeted her the way he couldn't a few minutes before.

IN CELEBRATION OF NICHOLAS AND MAREK'S RETURN, LULA planned a large outdoor picnic with the entire clan. Alius's mother was still in town and his father, Kev, had also joined, anticipating the arrival of their first grandchild.

Nicholas and Lula stayed up half the night as she listened to Nicholas's emotional tale of meeting and saying goodbye to his father, then the joyful reunion at the orphanage. Marek fell fast asleep on the hay padded mattress in front of the fire, while Nicholas and Lula fell asleep in each other's arms and woke to the bright sunlight rising over the apple trees.

Lula spread multi-colored cloths over the wooden picnic tables outside as Nicholas assisted in bringing out cooked sausages, cabbage and boiled potatoes. Marek followed Nicholas everywhere, as if he didn't trust anyone else. He knew it would take time for the child to be at ease, but he hoped it was sooner rather than later.

All at once, a loud, boisterous voice sounded from the front of the cottage as a wagon pulled forward. Goldie stood up before it rolled to a stop, shouting, "I have the pies! I hope you didn't go to any trouble!"

"For heaven's sake, Goldie, Sit down before you fall off the wagon!" a deep voice growled.

"Hush now, you old fool!" she spat.

Nicholas glanced toward Lula with wide eyes, and Marek cowered behind Nicholas's legs with his hands covering his ears.

She smirked. "I forgot you haven't met Alius's father."

"Who's the blonde with the crazy hair?" he whispered.

Lula giggled. "That's Alius's sister, Tina. Sweet girl, but a bit loony."

"So like the rest of the family?" he asked.

Lula nodded as everyone unloaded from the wagon. "Exactly."

"Nicholas, my boy! Glad to have you back," Goldie called out. "Your lady has been pining for you, she has." Goldie placed a big sloppy kiss on Nicholas's cheek, then peeked over toward Marek. "Who have we got here?"

"This is Marek. Marek Klaus," Nicholas added. Everyone's eyes widened at the surprise introduction, but Goldie smiled down at the boy unphased. "Glad to meet you Marek. I'm Goldie, but you, sweet child, can call me Nana."

Marek looked around nervously.

"He, um, doesn't speak," Lula whispered.

Goldie threw her hands up. "Thank heavens for that. Someone tell me where I can get one of those!" She glared at her husband, then walked toward the picnic table.

Nicholas glanced over toward Lula and raised a brow.

A large lad, with crazy red hair like Alius stepped forward with his hand out in greeting. "I'm Alius's father, Kev. But you can call me Ruder."

Nicholas stepped closer, afraid he didn't hear him right. "I'm sorry? Ruder?"

"That's right." Ruder smiled and nodded. "Got that nickname from my lovebug over there. I guess it stuck."

A large pie dish was thrust into Nicholas's hands as Tina stood before him with a too-wide smile, almost uncomfortable. Then she walked away without a word.

Nicholas nodded, greeting the odd girl, then his eyes widened as Alius assisted his larger-than-life wife toward the table.

Nicholas scratched the back of his neck and cleared his throat. "Wow, Minna. You look . . ."

"Choose your words wisely, Nicholas Klaus." She glared from across the lawn.

Nicholas swallowed, nervous there wouldn't be anything he could say that wouldn't insult her. "You're glowing." Had he only been away for two weeks? She was huge.

"Hmph," she grumbled. "Glowing like Franz's backside you mean."

Alius snickered behind her, but froze when she turned, scowling.

"Oh, Minna. You look lovely, sweet friend. Come sit next to me," Lula called out.

Minna's expression softened as she waddled her way toward Lula. "Oh, thank you, Lula. I do appreciate the compliment. You're too sweet," she mumbled while glaring at Alius.

Nicholas clapped Alius on the back. There were no words.

After a somewhat loud and entertaining lunch, the women accompanied Minna inside to rest and Ruder followed Nicholas, Marek, and Alius to the barn to inspect their handiwork. He turned each wood carving from side to side, running his thick calloused fingers over the smooth ridges to check for flaws.

"Alius, my boy, you've done a fine job. You must have had an excellent teacher." Ruder chuckled and elbowed Nicholas at the joke. "I remember the lad carving stick-men as a child.

Now, here he is creating detailed soldiers and horses. Fine work."

Alius grinned at the compliment. "Hey there, Marek. Can you do something for me? Maybe you can test one of these out, you know. Let me know if the children will like them." He held out a small carving of a horse and Marek smiled.

"ALIUS REALLY HAS BROUGHT SO MUCH JOY TO THE CHILDREN during Christmas. I can't explain the feeling of watching them open a toy they would have never gotten if it weren't for his hard work," Nicholas added.

"Ah, now. You and Eulas are the ones who started it all—giving most of your rations away to feed the hungry. I'm just trying to bring a little joy to the kids as well." Alius blushed.

"It's brilliant," Ruder replied. "All of it. I hope you'll allow me to help this year."

Alius's mouth fell open. "Blimey, Pa. With you helping we could make enough toys for the whole town. What do you think, Nicholas?"

He jolted as if in a daze. "Yes, of course. We'd love for you to help." He shuffled from side to side. "I've been trying to figure out a way to reach more families, but we really need more space to work and store toys."

"You don't mean leaving the farm, do you Nic? I thought you loved it here," Alius said, surprised.

"I do love it, Al, but I'm not sure this is where I'm meant to stay, you know? What if there's more?"

"Please tell me this isn't happening!" A shocked voice shrieked by the door.

The three men spun toward Minna, staring at them with wide eyes.

Nicholas immediately felt horrible. "I'm sorry, Minna. I'm

only thinking out loud—it doesn't mean we're going anywhere," Nicholas promised.

Minna shook her head back and forth with her mouth hanging open. Then, she looked down at the puddle on the ground.

The men froze, staring in shock. Alius pointed toward her feet, his shaky finger suspended in mid-air. "That's . . . that's not supposed to happen." He turned toward his father. "Right, Pa?"

Ruder clutched the carved soldier in his hands as his face paled. "Um. Well, Son. I'm quite certain this is usually where I passed out." He chuckled awkwardly before hurrying toward the door.

Then, Ruder turned to thrust the toy into Nicholas's hands before spinning back to Minna.

Alius and Nicholas spun, running into each other as if no one knew what to do, and Marek froze in fear.

By the time they made their way out of the barn, falling all over each other, Minna had waddled across the yard—crying out for her mother-in-law.

NICHOLAS SAT, WATCHING HIS FRIEND PACE THE LENGTH OF the porch, as the soft murmurs from Goldie mixed with the agitated and angry screams of Minna filled the air.

"It's too early, Nic. What if it's too soon? Do you think he'll be alright?"

Nicholas's eyes widened. "He?"

Alius shrugged. "Just a feeling."

"I don't know, Al. Maybe she was further along than you realized. I'm sure everything will be okay. Your mother will take care of her, you know that."

Alius nodded in agreement, then turned to continue pacing.

"Aahhh!" Minna cried. "Where is Alius?" She yelled from inside the cottage.

Alius spun toward the door. "Right here, Love. I'm coming!"

"Get him in here! I want to look him in the eye before I strangle him! I want to see the life leave his beady eyes!"

Marek gripped Nicholas's leg in fear.

Alius froze at the door and swallowed the lump in his throat. "Maybe I'll just wait out here."

"Smart boy, you are," Ruder called out. He leaned against the wooden post, pale and sweaty.

Minna screamed, loud and painful, as Alius covered his ears along with Marek, unable to listen. All at once, there was silence.

Nicholas scurried to his feet as the soft whimper of a baby turned into a full-on wail. Alius slowly lowered his hands, his eyes fixed on the wooden door of the house. Minutes felt like hours as they waited for news. Lula opened the door, clutching a small bundle against her chest. Her eyes were full of tears as the intensity of her gaze met Nicholas's.

Time seemed to pause, as everyone stared at the infant in her arms.

The baby grunted and she jolted, turning toward Alius. She hid her emotions behind a smile. "You have a daughter. A beautiful, perfect baby girl."

Alius glanced down at the blanket as if an imposter hid underneath. "Are you certain?"

Lula nodded. "She's a little small, but Goldie said her lungs are strong."

All at once, Minna cried out and fear took root, interrupting the intimate moment.

Alius took a step back. "What's wrong with Minna? Something is wrong with my wife!"

Lula shook her head. "I don't know. Here, take the baby."

Alius's shaky hands wrapped around the bundle as Lula ran back inside. He patted and clutched his baby girl to his chest, but Nicholas knew he couldn't truly enjoy the moment, not while worrying over his wife. An eerie silence took hold, and Alius leaned back as if he'd pass out.

Nicholas stepped forward. "Hey, Al. Why don't you let me take the baby? You have a lot going on right now. Alright?"

Alius nodded, without taking his eyes off the door. "Sure, Nic. Yeah."

Nicholas laid the newborn on his chest, just as Lula shuffled back outside.

She smiled through tears and stepped forward. "Alius? I'd like you to meet your other daughter."

Alius stepped back, hitting the post of the porch. Ruder sat in the rocking chair, unable to handle the excitement of the day, wiping the sweat from his brow.

"What did you say?" Alius asked. Sweat dripped from his too-long nose as the color drained from his face.

Lula giggled from excitement. "You have a second daughter."

Alius looked down at Lula's arms, then back at Nicholas. He looked from child to child, then frowned as if he'd cry. All at once, his legs gave way and he tumbled to the ground—the same time Minna cried out in pain.

THE SMALL COTTAGE WAS FILLED WITH FRIENDS AS NICHOLAS backed into a corner with Marek, attempting to stay out of the way. Alius sat in a chair beside Minna, with his two daughters sleeping against his chest. Minna glared at Alius from her bed, while holding their third baby girl in her arms.

"What a precious gift!" Goldie exclaimed. "Just look at that red hair on my grandbabies. They are beautiful."

Alius continued to stare at the floor, unable to meet Minna's death stare.

Lula pursed her lips, and Nicholas knew she was feeling the tension as well. Minna needed time to process everything and a crowd wouldn't help.

"I'm going to check on the animals," Nicholas announced while backing toward the door.

Alius narrowed his eyes as if Nicholas was abandoning him. He clenched his jaw and jerked his head to the seat beside him. Nicholas pretended to be oblivious.

"So if you need anything . . ." He quickly shut the door behind him and Marek followed suit.

23

LULA

*L*ula watched as Minna fed one of her daughters, the second held by Alius's sister, Tina, and the third asleep on Lula's chest. Minna appeared overwhelmed and annoyed at Alius for the current predicament, but the facade wasn't successful.

Everytime she twisted the tiny red curl on top of one of her daughter's heads, her warm eyes brightened, as if her whole world was tucked into those soft white blankets. Alius snored on the floor beside Minna while Goldie paced from one end of the cottage to the next, unable to accept the fact there was nothing to do at that moment.

"Goldie, would you mind holding this little one while I check on Nicholas and Marek? They've been gone for quite some time."

Goldie's eyes lit up at the request. "Of course, dear. Let me see . . . now which one do you have?"

Minna rolled her eyes. "That's Francis, named after my mum. You can tell by the dimple in her chin. Betty, named after Lula's mum, has the most hair and Annie, named after you, cries all the time." Minna smirked.

Goldie nodded happily, then froze as she processed her words.

Lula needed to escape. Quickly.

She handed the baby to Goldie and hurried out of the cottage. She walked the expanse of the orchards, the apple trees heavy with ripened fruit, then searched inside the barn, but Nicholas and Marek were nowhere to be found.

Slight movement across the field caught her attention and she stood perfectly still, waiting to see if she had imagined it. She eased closer until Marek and Nicholas came into view under the old birch tree in the distance. Lula stepped softly so she didn't disturb them and stopped when close enough to hear their conversation.

Lula smiled at the sight of Marek sitting beside Nicholas, arms resting on their knees, facing the old tree.

"This was my father's favorite tree. Well, not my real father, but that's a story for another day. This is the man who taught me about life. Eulas taught me what it means to work hard and love harder. I wouldn't be the man I am today without him, Marek. Sometimes I come here to feel closer to him."

Marek tilted his head back and smiled at Nicholas. Lula imagined Marek felt the same way about the man who took him from the orphanage and gave him a home.

A family.

"The most important gift Eulas ever gave me was his love. His love for people, for kindness, and for Christmas. Do you know what Christmas is?"

Marek shrugged as if he wasn't sure.

"Well, that's okay. We'll teach you. One day, you'll be preparing for your own Christmas Eve deliveries. Isn't that something?" He grinned down at the boy, then turned back to the tree.

"Sometimes I wonder if this is where I'm supposed to be,

you know? I can't help but feel as though this is just a stop along the way to something . . . bigger. Something profound. I know Lula is happy here, and I don't want to do anything to hurt her."

Nicholas sighed as he focused on the birch tree. "I'm trusting you, Eulas. I need to know when the time is right."

Lula quietly stepped back toward the house, Nicholas's words heavy on her heart. Had he always felt this way? Did he not want to raise their children here? She always knew the desires of his heart far outweighed her own. Lula considered herself a simple woman, wanting nothing more than a home to raise her family, but she wanted Nicholas to be happy. She would follow him to the end of the earth if that's what it took.

She wasn't ready to go back to the cottage. Overwhelmed by emotions, she needed a few minutes alone to sort through her thoughts. Chickens pecked around the outside of the barn as she eased the door open. There was peace inside the dark, musty building, as if the outside world didn't exist.

Lula raked and shoveled Franz's pen, replacing the coup with fresh hay. Then, she sat in the back corner of the barn, staring at the multitudes of wood-carved toys, bags of potatoes and apples to be simmered for jam. Nicholas poured his heart into every needy family at Christmas and loved every orphan as if they were his own. She grinned at the thought of him with Marek—the bond that had already begun to form. Lula clutched the fabric of her dress across her belly and closed her eyes.

She hadn't told him yet.

The last thing she wanted to do was keep something so monumental from him, but fear lingered in the back of her mind. What if something happened? What if she lost it? Lula shook off the dark thoughts that threatened their happiness.

They deserved this.

All of them, including Marek, deserved a family.

Lula pushed to her feet, but froze when she noticed a rusty latch raised from the wooden slab of the barn floor, as if someone forgot to lock it. Sweeping the hay aside, her eyes widened at the sight of the hidden door she never realized was there. She glanced from side to side, as if she feared being caught.

She pulled on the door and the splintered wood whined as if disgruntled by the disturbance. A small, delicately carved oak box sat alone on the ground underneath the floor. Pulling the box into her lap, she rubbed across the top with one finger. There was very little dust. This was not an object that had sat untouched.

For some reason, that made her nervous. Was this a secret? Did she have any right to open it? All reason dissipated as curiosity won out. She lifted the lid and gasped at the large stack of bills bundled together by straw. Underneath, lay a worn parchment with faded edges and torn corners. Lula carefully unfolded what looked like a map, along with writing she didn't understand.

"What is this?" she whispered to herself.

"It's a map." Nicholas called out.

Lula jumped to her feet, dropping the parchment on the ground. "Nicholas, I'm so sorry. Curiosity got the best of me, I guess." She lowered her head, ashamed, as the toes of his boots stopped in front of her.

Nicholas lifted her chin and smiled. "There's nothing I won't tell you, Lula. I guess I've just struggled with some of this since Eulas passed."

"This was his?"

Nicholas nodded. "He left it for me—for us."

She shook her head, confused. "I don't understand. Where does it lead?"

He sighed. "Magisfjell." Nicholas picked up the map from

the floor and pointed out the isolated island of ice. "Eulas dreamt of seeing it one day. I think he hoped I would find it since he never got the chance."

Lula studied the paper in his hands. He wanted this. He yearned to discover this land that meant so much to Eulas—she could see it in his eyes.

"Maybe we should go."

Nicholas raised his brows. "Go?"

Lula nodded. She refused to hold him back. If this was something that called out to him, then she would be with him every step of the way. "That's right. An adventure, don't you think?"

"Lula, we have a family here in Brusberg. Plus, we know nothing about this place. What about Marek?"

"Of course. Why would a small boy care anything about going on an adventure? He will be appalled!" Lula threw her hand over her chest, dramatically.

"Funny girl." Nicholas smirked. "We can't just leave Alius and Minna, especially not right now, Lu. We're still preparing for Christmas . . ."

"Stop making excuses, Nicholas. You're restless. I can see it in everything you do and maybe it's because you're fighting what Eulas is guiding you toward."

Nicholas clenched his jaw.

She knew she had struck a nerve.

"You don't even know if it's real." He whispered.

"You don't know that it isn't."

For the first time in her life, she saw fear in his eyes. That's when she knew—Nicholas was trying to protect his family. This drive, this need to be a part of something bigger had always been inside of him, and it would never go away. She refused to let him ignore it.

She pulled the map from his hands, rolling it up with more sass than necessary, refusing to meet his gaze.

"Lu, what are you doing?"

"I'm taking this map to Benson. See if he can help me decipher it and find the island."

Nicholas stepped forward. "You can't do that!"

Lula stopped on her way out the door and looked over her shoulder. "Watch me."

"I've seen it, years ago. Got chartered by a Klaus brother. Where did you get it?" Benson asked as he and George sat across from Nicholas and Lula in the cottage.

Nicholas sighed. "Eulas left it to me. Can you take us there?"

Benson sat back in his chair and sighed.

George grumbled, "What is it with you Klaus's and your determination for adventure?"

Nicholas grinned. "Is that a yes?"

"I can get you within one to two kilometers from the main island, but not closer. The ice is too thick."

Lula's brows pulled together in confusion. "So how do we get there?"

"You'll have to take a canoe to shore, maneuver around the small ice caps. It won't be easy."

Lula's eyes widened in surprise. "I see." A moment of fear took root as her hand gently glided over her belly.

"Not saying it won't be worth it—if you make it. Even at a distance, I've never seen anything like it. What do you plan on doing when you get there?"

"Eulas said there are caves for shelter and the fish are plentiful. We'll take some food and supplies to get us by until you return in a week or so."

Benson clenched his jaw, uncomfortable with the idea.

"We just want to see it with our own eyes, Benson. It was important to Eulas."

He frowned, but nodded in agreement.

"How long will it take?" Lula asked.

George replied, "A week, maybe more depending on the weather."

Nicholas glanced toward Lula and his eyes softened. "What do you think?"

She watched him—the seconds that drifted by felt like hours. Was this the best time? Would there ever be a good time? The desire that had been planted inside of Nicholas would never falter.

She knew that with all of her heart.

She cleared her throat and spoke with confidence. "When can we leave?"

George shook his head as he stood. "You're all bloody insane, I tell ya. No way will Sheila agree to me sailing back to that mountain. I've done it once. Won't do it again. Too risky."

Benson pursed his lips. "I have a break in shipments coming up—a couple weeks maybe."

"Are you listening to yourself? Staci will have your head, I tell ya!" George shouted.

"I'm staying far enough back from the ice, George. I shouldn't have a problem if I don't try to maneuver through the bergs."

"And you," George continued. "What about your farm? Christmas for the families? You have responsibilities here."

Nicholas nodded. "We almost have a full stock for Christmas Eve already. Alius and Minna have agreed to care for the farm until we return and we will be back before the holidays."

"Aye. Got it all worked out, do ya? I still think you're shy of a pint!"

Nicholas turned his head toward Lula, and gripped her small hand in his large calloused palm. He waited, as if expecting her to back out.

She took a deep breath. "We've never been one to turn our back on an adventure."

Nicholas grinned.

"Are you mad?" Minna shouted.

Lula glared at Minna, whispering, "Keep your voice down."

"You still haven't told him? You know he'd never let you go on this trip if he knew, Lula." Minna cradled one of her daughters against her chest, gently bouncing the irritable newborn.

Lula continued packing as if Minna hadn't spoken. All at once, Minna reached forward with her free arm and gripped Lula's hand. "You're afraid, aren't you? Afraid you will lose the baby, so you don't want to tell him."

Her lip quivered as Minna's words hit home. Lula slowly sat on the edge of the bed for fear of her shaky knees giving way. Her voice was barely more than a whisper as she failed to hold the heartache inside.

"There have been others, Minna." Lula shook her head as tears filled her eyes. "There's been too much loss already. I don't want him to know he married a flawed, inadequate wife. I can't take it anymore."

Minna sat down beside her. "How many?"

"Three."

"He doesn't know about any of them?" Minna asked.

Lula shook her head. "They were early on. I couldn't stand the thought of his sympathetic eyes. What kind of wife am I if I can't give him a child?"

"You know he would never think less of you, Lula. How far along do you think you are?"

"A few months now."

Minna's eyes brightened. "Blimey, Lula, that's wonderful. You could give birth by the end of the year."

Lula shook her head. "I don't want to talk about it . . . just in case. Okay, Minna?"

"Alright. But if you haven't told him by the time you get back, I will."

Lula nodded. "Deal."

"ALL GOOD?" BENSON CALLED OUT.

Nicholas led Lula and Marek onboard, carrying his fishing pole in hand. When Lula had questioned his supplies, he explained that they needed to be able to fish and hunt if needed. Her face flushed from embarrassment. She should have thought of that.

Eulas had told Nicholas his father used caves for shelter, so they were depending on those while there. Lula packed a satchel of potatoes, apples and preserves in case they struggled to find food.

She stepped off the dock and climbed over the railing into Benson's ship. The rocking of the deck took her off guard and her head spun as she stumbled forward. Nicholas's strong arms wrapped around her waist as his forehead wrinkled in concern.

"Are you alright, Lu?"

She nodded, but refused to look him in the eyes. "Sorry. I'm so sorry."

He chuckled. "What are you apologizing for?"

Lula didn't answer. She took a deep breath, shook off the dizziness, and turned to offer Marek a hand. Nicholas stepped forward and lifted the boy effortlessly. He turned, kissed her on the head and continued storing their belongings.

Lula glanced down at Marek and smiled, hoping to appear at ease. Marek didn't look concerned in the least. His shaggy brown hair swept across his forehead and the deep brown depths of his eyes lit up with excitement. "Are you ready for our adventure?"

As usual, Marek didn't answer, but he couldn't hide his grin. When the child smiled, it lit up an entire room.

All at once, Lulas's head spun once again, and nausea rolled through her body like a wave. She'd been lucky enough to avoid morning sickness, so she wasn't sure why she felt so uneasy. She reached for the railing of the boat and inhaled slowly. "How about we find a comfortable place to sit? Someplace warm?"

Marek's small hand slid into Lula's, and her chest tightened when he gripped her palm, as if he knew she needed the comfort. Then, he led her into the cabin.

24

NICHOLAS

*M*arek squealed in fear as waves crashed into the thin glass of the cabin window. The angry sea tossed and spun the ship as if determined to swallow them whole. Nicholas stumbled forward as the boards under his feet shook from the onslaught of ice and water.

What had he done?

Lula's tight-lipped expression was the only indication of her distress. She whispered words of comfort to Marek, promising to protect him with her life. Nicholas's guilt would kill him before the storm did.

He just knew it.

Benson stood at the wheel, maneuvering through the waves as they crashed overhead. Chunks of ice slid across the deck, washed up from the raging sea. Right as an enormous swell lifted the boat into the air, the wave collapsed, slamming the vessel back into the frigid, frightening waters.

Benson turned, tossing cork vests into Nicholas's arms, then spun back toward the wheel to fight the thrashing of the storm. Nicholas fell to his knees, hurrying to wrap the vest around Marek, and another around Lula. His hands shook as the boat tipped, throwing him against the cabin door. The small hinges gave way, ripping the door off the cabin and into the air like a kite. Nicholas gripped the side of the doorframe, fighting to pull himself inside, while Lula clung to his wrist with all of her strength.

All of a sudden, the boat tipped upright and he slid forward, knocking Benson off his feet. Benson reached toward the wheel to catch his balance and spun the boat into the oncoming wave. When he regained control, a loud crack of thunder rolled across the ominous sky overhead, as if growling from fury.

They would make it. They had to.

Nicholas bowed his head in the midst of the storm, crying out, "If this is where you want me, save us. Please . . . save my family."

NICHOLAS STOOD ON DECK AS SNOW CONTINUED TO FALL, thick flakes of ice biting his cheeks and nose. It had been a rough trip—more treacherous than he ever imagined. Benson was right, the combination of ice and sea this far north was brutal and he now understood why George was against it.

Benson had taken them around several storms producing waves taller than the ship. On more than one occasion, Nicholas called out to God for protection over his family. It had taken a couple of extra days at sea, but they were finally getting close.

He turned his gaze to the cabin, where Lula sat weak and pale. Worry over his wife overpowered everything else at the moment. Marek could sense it too—he hadn't left her side. Her lack of appetite could have been due to the rough sea, but he knew it was more. He'd tried to give her space the past few days, let her come to him when ready, but his patience had run out. She was hiding something from him.

Protecting him.

It was his job to protect her.

He walked into the cabin where Benson stood with a mug of hot coffee. Nicholas smiled down at Marek, attempting to warm Lula's shivering frame. "Hey buddy. How about you let me take over, okay?" Nicholas whispered.

Marek raised his head and stared at him as if thinking it over.

"I'll keep her warm. I promise," Nicholas assured him.

Marek's lips tightened as if unhappy, but he hesitantly slid down the small wooden bench, leaving just enough room for Nicholas to sit. He apparently wasn't going far.

Nicholas pulled Lula into his side and swept his palm across her forehead. She stirred and snuggled deeper into the warmth of his body. "Lu? What's going on? I need you to talk to me."

"Just a little sea-sick. I'll be fine when we get there."

He narrowed his eyes. "There's something else."

Lula tilted her head back, meeting his gaze as she chewed the side of her lip.

"Hey, Marek. I think I see a whale portside. Wanna take a closer look?" Benson asked.

Marek stretched his neck out the cabin window, intrigued.

Benson held his hand out, "Come now. We'll be right back." Benson winked at Nicholas as he led the boy onto the deck.

Nicholas squatted down in front of Lula, cupping the sides of her face to meet her exhausted eyes. "It's my job to take care of you. If you're sick I need to know, Lu. You've never been sea-sick in your life, so what's wrong?"

Tears filled her eyes and she sighed in defeat. She lowered her head and he watched as her chin trembled.

"I'm so scared, Nicholas," she admitted.

He shook his head, confused. "Scared of what? I won't let anything happen to you. You know that."

She gripped the fabric at her waist and swallowed.

"Lula?" Nicholas tilted her chin up, determined to hear the truth.

"I'm pregnant," she whispered.

Nicholas deflated, as his gaze traveled down her body. He leaned forward, placing his hands on her belly as he closed his eyes. "Are you sure?"

Lula nodded and ran her fingers through his hair. "I guess pregnancy and the rough sea make a bad combination."

His gaze met hers. "How far?"

She shrugged and turned away as if ashamed. "A few months."

Nicholas jerked his head back as if he'd been slapped. "Why didn't you tell me?"

She threw her hand over her mouth to muffle the sob. "Because there have been others. I'm so scared, Nicholas. I don't want to fail you."

He would never be able to describe the pain of seeing her so defeated. Knowing she endured that type of loss and disappointment alone tormented him. "You could never fail me, Lu. I don't understand why things happen, but I have to trust in the plan God has for our family. You have to trust in me to be there for you."

She nodded. "You're right. I'm sorry."

"And you should have told me before we left for this trip. I would have refused to go, but I think you know that."

She leaned forward. "I knew we were supposed to come, Nicholas. I can't explain it."

He shook his head and breathed to calm himself.

"Nothing we can do now. I need you to rest and eat something—anything. When we get to the island, I'll find shelter. Promise me you won't push yourself too hard."

"I promise."

Nicholas palmed her face once more and pulled her forward to meet his lips. He smiled as his mouth brushed across hers. "We're gonna have a baby."

She grinned. "We're gonna have a baby."

"Are you sure we can't get any closer?" Nicholas asked. Thick flakes of snow clouded the air around him, making it hard to see. Nicholas squinted toward the dark shadow of the crest of Magisfjell, but in the darkness he could barely make out the outline.

"Afraid not. We'd risk damaging the boat and then none of us would ever get off this bloody island."

Nicholas nodded. "Then I'll paddle the rest of the way."

"Won't be easy, Mate."

Nicholas grinned. "That's why I brought Marek. He'll be doing most of the work."

They looked down into the wide eyes of the boy and chuckled at his horrified expression.

"Just kidding, Marek. You keep Lula warm, alright?"

He nodded, relieved.

Benson and Nicholas lowered the paddle boat into the dark slush of ice with ropes, then loaded their gear and supplies for the coming weeks. Benson would return in two weeks time to take them home. Nicholas wasn't certain what they would find—but he'd never have peace until he knew for sure.

He reached his hand out toward Benson and nodded. "Thanks again. For everything."

Benson chuckled. "Still hard to believe you're the same scrawny boy that washed up in Brusberg that day." His laughter faded as his eyes filled with concern. "Take care of yourself." He nodded toward Lula and Marek. "Take care of them."

Nicholas's gaze traveled across the black ice surrounding the boat and he took a deep breath. "On my life."

He climbed down into the paddle boat, then Benson lowered Lula and Marek into his waiting arms. He huddled them together, wrapped in blankets, then gave one last wave as Benson tipped his hat goodbye.

Nicholas began a steady, strong pace as he paddled toward land, determined to find shelter as soon as possible. Minutes felt like hours as the front of the boat fought against the thick ice blocking their path. He ignored the stinging bite of sleet against his face, and the strain of his muscles as he breathed through painful cramps.

His heart pounded, but had little to do with the physical strain and everything to do with Magisfjell. A sensation—almost a tingling—intensified at the proximity of the mystical mountain.

By the time the paddle boat scraped against the frozen bank of the island, Nicholas couldn't feel the tips of his fingers. Crystals of ice coated his eyelashes and his arms shook from exertion.

"Everyone alright?"

Lula and Marek were covered from head to toe with the thick wool blanket. He could barely make out their form in the dark.

"We're okay," Lula called out.

Nicholas stepped onto the snowbank, pulling the boat in as far as possible, then helped Lula and Marek to shore. He unloaded the supplies, stacking them under a large cypress tree that had to be a hundred years old. He tied the boat to the trunk of the tree, then turned toward his wife.

He faltered as he took in Lula's wide eyes and open mouth. She shook her head in disbelief. Nicholas followed her gaze over his shoulder and he stumbled back at the sight of the sharp cliff edges of stone and ice stacked high above them. Tall trees created a canopy overhead and branches hung heavy with snow.

Although magnificent, the island wasn't what shocked them the most.

A herd of deer, close to a dozen, stood frozen, their dark eyes focused on Nicholas. Antlers like he had never seen before stood tall and wide, branching off in all directions. Thick cream-colored fur covered their flank and transformed into a dark brownish gray on their hind legs.

All but one.

He was the leader—the alpha. Taller than the rest, there wasn't a speck of color to be found. Solid white from the tips of his ears to his hooves, intelligence filled the pink of his eyes, as if he knew more about Nicholas than he did himself. He sniffed the air, his solid pink nose rising toward them as moonlight glinted off the tip, intensifying the color. The deer stepped forward and Lula stumbled back, leaning against Nicholas with her arms clutching Marek.

Marek tilted his head to the side, then eased his toe forward. Lula's grip tightened and Marek pulled free, completely focused on the animal in front of him. Lula reached to stop him, but Nicholas pulled her back.

"Wait," he whispered as he watched Marek step directly in front of the deer.

There was a connection—something that bonded him to the animal at first glance. Nicholas couldn't help but think it was because he was different. He stood out among the pack, just like Marek stood out from other children. The boy's hand slowly slid up the snout of the deer and the animal snorted his approval. The deer leaned down, pressing against Marek's forehead and Lula gasped.

Marek looked over his shoulder at Lula's tear-filled gaze and grinned.

"Don't . . . don't worry Moo. Mothh, Mother. He's my fri —friend."

Lula clutched the wool coat at her chest as if she could relieve the pressure building inside of her. Nicholas exhaled, overwhelmed by emotion. Tears filled his eyes at Marek's first words since . . . when? When was the last time the boy cared about anything enough to speak?

All at once, the white deer stepped toward Nicholas and lowered it's head in respect, then quickly popped up, leading the herd across the snow-covered mountain.

Lula leaned forward to watch them run away. "Where are they going?"

"They'll be back," Nicholas told her.

"How do you know?" She asked.

He chuckled and rumpled Marek's hair. "Because they made a friend."

Marek grinned. "Ru."

"Ru?" Lula asked. "Have you named him already?"

Marek grinned a toothy smile.

Nicholas chuckled. "Come on. Let's get you both out of this weather."

He caught sight of a rock path past the large tree and led Lula and Marek toward the mountainside. A small crevice toward the base of the rock caught his attention, and he frowned as he kneeled to take a closer look. The surface of the inside was smooth as glass. It wasn't any bigger than the canoe out front, but it would protect them from the frigid wind for now. Lula and Marek crawled on all fours inside the pitiful excuse for shelter, shivering.

Lula peeked up at him, frowning. "Please tell me this isn't the cave Eulas referred to."

Nicholas had more faith in him than that, but fear kept him from replying. "Let's get you out of the wind for now, we'll look for better shelter later." He unfolded the wool blankets from his pack, wrapping them snug around Lula and Marek. Then, he pulled a box of matches from his pocket, soggy from the seawater.

Lula's brows raised and she grimaced. "I'm not sure we'll make it without fire, Nicholas."

He wanted to scream.

He needed to throw something.

Frustration hummed around him, sucking the life out of his drained body and mind. Nicholas took a deep breath and settled beside them, blocking them from the wind that seeped through the small opening in the rocks. He wrapped his arm around Lula as Marek snuggled up to her other side.

The last week had caught up with all of them, mentally and physically. Within minutes, Lula and Marek's breathing evened out as exhaustion prevailed. Nicholas closed his eyes, but sleep never came. They had several hours until sunrise and worry over his family overpowered the fatigue.

He didn't know what to do. Eulas would tell him to pray, but he hated himself for only talking to God when he needed him. Shouldn't he reach out to him everyday? Guilt flooded his heart and mind.

"I'll do better. I promise," he whispered. "Please, Lord. Please let this desire to come here have little to do with my own selfishness and everything to do with the path you are laying before me. Please give me guidance and wisdom."

Nicholas glanced down as Lula's body began shivering from head to toe. He eased out from under her weight and she stirred.

Nicholas whispered. "Stay here. Alright?"

"Where are you going?" Lula asked.

"I'll be back, I promise."

Nicholas crawled out of the small shelter and blinked against the icy needles beating against his face. In the distance, a herd of deer halted—staring at him as if he were trespassing on their territory. But then, one of the biggest, darkest deer stepped forward, alternating his front hooves in place, prancing. Then he snorted toward his direction and took off to the back side of the mountain.

Nicholas had the strange feeling he was supposed to follow. "Where are you taking me, Prancer?"

He shuffled through the thick snow as slush crept in the top of his boots and clung to his socks. An iridescent shimmer outlined his footprints in the snow and left a magical path of light behind him. Nicholas pulled his hat lower to cover his ears as he struggled to adjust his eyes in the darkness ahead. The deer he referred to as Prancer turned a sharp corner and Nicholas froze. Hidden underneath the cliffside, steps had been carved into the stone rising high above him. He would never have found it in the dark without help.

Wherever it led, it had to be better than the den they were currently sleeping in. Nicholas quickly shuffled through the snow, back to Lula and Marek. Lula jolted as soon as Nicholas crawled back into their cave, but Marek took more effort to wake. The small boy struggled to shuffle through the new fallen snow, so Nicholas hoisted the child on his back and pushed forward.

Lula gasped as she took in the narrow length of steps. "Where do you think it goes?"

"I'm hoping it leads to shelter. Someone has obviously been up this path before," he explained.

All at once, Marek jumped from his back and ran toward the shoreline.

"Marek! Stop!" Nicholas shouted.

Marek halted and tilted his head toward the sky. Flashes of green and pink reflected in the brown of his eyes and Nicholas spun to look toward the stars. He stumbled back in awe at the magical swirl of colors overhead, spanning from one side to another. He'd never seen anything like it.

"That is the most magical thing I've ever seen," Lula whispered.

Nicholas wrapped his arms around her and smiled. "It is. Let's get you out of the wind." He guided her toward the steps and called for Marek to follow.

Lula stopped, gripping the sleeve of his coat. "There's something intense about this place. Not really ominous, but watchful." She glanced around as if being watched. All at once, the limbs of nearby trees swayed back and forth, as if acknowledging her observation.

Nicholas surveyed the path and frowned. "Yeah, I know. Let's go."

They eased up the rocks, careful to avoid the ice that had recently formed in spots. The stone wall of the mountain stood on each side of the stairwell, offering stability if they started to slip. Nicholas couldn't help but notice the silver tint sparkling in the stone, a gleaming combination of colors.

The top of the steps led into a cave-like corridor, protected from the wind and ice. A series of wood-planked doors had been built into the stone wall and Nicholas froze, confused by the sight.

Lula ran her fingers over the metal hinges. "What is this place?"

Nicholas shook his head. "I don't know."

His heart pounded as he pushed on the frozen door handle. The hinges creaked, but gave way into darkness. Nicholas wanted to turn around—take Lula and Marek back to Brusberg where he knew it was safe.

He couldn't.

Something inside of him pushed him forward, urging him to take a closer look. "Stay here," he ordered.

Without a sliver of moonlight, the windowless room was black as the night sky. Nicholas ran his hands across what felt like a table, searching for anything to illuminate the room. He shuffled from corner to corner, until a small hand tugged on his trousers to get his attention. Marek held up a box of matches and smiled, the white of his teeth the only thing visible from his proud expression.

"Good man, Marek."

Nicholas struck a match and his breath caught at the sight of a small bed, stone fireplace and table covered in parchments. The wood inside the hearth had long been dried and it flamed to life the moment he threw the match forward.

Lula and Marek stepped toward the warmth of the fire while Nicholas located a lantern in the corner of the room. It appeared as if nothing had been touched for years. He held the lantern over scattered papers, books and photographs, shuffling through the collection for anything to help him understand his place in such a mysterious land.

Then he found it.

A photograph, faded and creased down the middle, had been tucked into a diary piled high with meaningless texts. A pale man with broad shoulders and a long white beard had his arm around a dark-skinned gentleman. They were looking down onto a crowd of children who were pulling at their thick red robes and satchels.

The children appeared malnourished and barely clothed. A thin, red-haired boy pulled a blanket out of the man's satchel and clutched it to his small frame, smiling. These men were taking care of the poor. Nicholas flipped the photo over and gasped.

In beautiful swirls of black ink, read, 'Larry Starosta and Ron Maxwell Klaus.'

He studied the names over and over, unable to make sense of the words. Starosta and Klaus? Together? What did it mean?

"Nicholas?" Lula called out. "What did you find?"

She stepped up beside him, taking the photo from his hand. "Starosta? Where have I heard that name before?"

Nicholas looked up, without really seeing anything in front of him. "My mother was Miriam Starosta," he softly whispered. "Goldie said my grandfather was an explorer."

Lula dropped the photo and stepped back as if burned. "I don't understand. How are they connected to the Klaus family? You didn't know who your family was when you met Eulas. This doesn't make any sense."

"I know." He rubbed his forehead, knowing the possibility of a coincidence was slim.

"What are you going to do?" she asked.

Nicholas exhaled and attempted to alleviate her distress. He turned around, pulling her against his chest. "I'm going to bring our supplies and food up to make sure you both are properly fed." He leaned forward and kissed her on the cheek. "We'll figure out the rest tomorrow."

As he walked out into the corridor, Nicholas closed the door behind him and leaned back against the cold stone wall. Something monumental was happening and he knew within the pit of his stomach that he would never be the same again. He stepped toward the opening in the cave and took a minute to appreciate the mesmerizing scene before him.

Large caps of ice washed ashore as thick snowflakes fell so slowly, they appeared to hover mid-air. The Northern Lights of the Aurora swirled overhead, vibrant and strong. Although mysterious, the air held a comforting peace that reminded him of Christmas morning.

A cold wind whipped across his face, but was soon replaced with warmth as he fell in love for the second time in his life.

Then, a deep, soulful hum vibrated throughout his chest —a timbre that reminded him of Eulas. Then the humming ceased, and Nicholas stumbled back as something inside of him whispered, "Welcome home."

25

NICHOLAS

The fading of soft embers woke him early the next morning as he fought to untangle himself from Lula. The small bed offered little comfort, considering his size, and he regretted not sleeping on the floor next to Marek.

After adding several logs to the dwindling fire, he tucked the blanket around Marek's shoulders and quietly dressed. The cave was a blessing and offered comfort and protection for not only Marek, but Lula, the mother of his child.

His child.

He still couldn't believe it. Nicholas already considered himself a father the day he met Marek, but he knew the desire to carry a baby was strong within Lula, and he wanted nothing more than to make her dreams come true.

He slipped out quietly and pulled his cane pole from the supplies outside the door. Eulas had always taught him to fish early, but he wasn't even certain what he would be fishing for.

"Help me out, Eulas. You wanted me here. Give me a little guidance."

Nicholas eased down the slippery path and walked around the backside of the island, searching for a convenient spot to cast his line. Seals lounged along large bergs around the mountainside, and thick sheets of ice bordered the shoreline.

He chose a dense patch of snow and ice along the side and walked out far enough for the line to reach the water. After a few minutes, he lost several pieces of stale bread to aggressive bites and grew excited over the possibility of fresh fish for dinner. A prickling sensation, almost a warning, ran along the back of his neck as the hair on his arms stood at attention.

Someone was there.

Nicholas scanned the island, his eyes searching every snow-covered tree and branch nearby. He jerked his head to the left as red eyes peered at him among the thick trees.

"Ru," he mumbled. "Sorry, Buddy. Marek's still asleep."

Nicholas smiled and stepped forward to cast his line once again. A crackle echoed in the air around him as the noise of the sea faded into the background. His heart pounded, but he stayed perfectly still. His gaze lowered to the toe of his boot where a small crack had formed underneath his sole.

Mentally, he ran through every reasonable option. He decided to slowly slide the opposite boot back to take the weight off his front leg. As soon as he slid back, the crack in the ice lengthened. He closed his eyes and prayed.

Small splinters of ice popped all at once, and Nicholas dove toward the shoreline, attempting to grasp something solid. The ice under his boots gave way, and as soon as the frigid water enveloped his legs, his muscles seized. He gripped the plate of ice with both arms, struggling to pull himself to shore.

Ru ran forward, distress evident by the bucking of hooves and snorting in the air. He stomped and kicked, too fearful to step onto the ice. Nicholas's hand slid and he clawed toward the surface with the tips of his fingers, unable to gain leverage. As soon as the ice broke away from the shore, a heart wrenching, high-pitched bark from Ru filled the air.

Then Nicholas went under.

The icy water wrapped around his arms and legs like a vise, limiting his movement. He pushed forward, and forced himself to the surface to take a deep breath. As if refusing to relent, the sea pulled him under once again and his body screamed for relief. He'd never felt so much fear and pain at one time.

He pushed forward again, but slammed his head against a thick sheet of ice. His hands moved frantically, searching for an opening in the slab as the current pulled him deeper into the ocean. Slushy seawater burned his eyes as the frozen water kept him captive. He beat the ice over and over as his lungs burned for relief.

His lips tightened as he fought against the urge to open his mouth, knowing the fate that awaited. His energy faded and it felt as though his knuckles beat against the ice in slow motion.

The morning sunlight shone across the surface as Nicholas's movements ceased. All at once, a shadow hovered over the ice. Dark and thin with a posture he knew all too well. Nicholas's eyes widened and knew with all of his heart he hadn't survived.

It was Eulas.

The shadow swung something over his shoulder, and the hard crunch of ice slammed overhead. Again and again, he beat against the ice until it buckled and cracked. He jerked Nicholas up by his collar, and as soon as his head broke the surface, he gasped for air.

He wanted to reach for support, but the frigid temps had numbed his hands, keeping him immobile. His body shook from the shock and he attempted to wipe the salt water from his eyes, but his fingers were useless.

The hold on his coat released and his shoulder hit the padding of snow. Nicholas fought to turn toward him. He needed to see for himself.

"Eulas! Eulas, is that you?" his scratchy voice called out, desperate.

"No, Son. I'm Phillip. Eulas's brother."

NICHOLAS SAT IN FRONT OF THE FIRE, WHILE LULA WRAPPED every available blanket around his shoulders. Phillip came back into the room with a mug of steaming liquid and held it out to him.

"It isn't good, but it'll warm you up."

Nicholas reached for the tin mug with shaking hands. "Thank you." He sipped slowly, letting the weak, hot coffee trickle down his throat. "You're right. It isn't good." Nicholas cut his eyes toward Phillip and grinned. He looked so much like Eulas, it hurt.

Phillip grunted deep and looked around the room. "Haven't been in this room in awhile."

"Was this Starosta's room?" Nicholas asked.

Phillip nodded. "Was once."

Nicholas sighed. "Look. I don't know what I'm doing here. How can something feel so right and so terrifying at the same time?"

Phillip grinned. "My brother give you that map?" he asked.

"Yes, Sir." Nicholas glanced down at the floor and sighed. "Eulas was like a father to me. I wouldn't have survived without him."

Phillip teared up, but quickly covered by clearing his

throat. "Sounds like him. He always wanted a child. After Alma died, he never was the same. I only wish we had kept in touch more than we did. Always tried to get him to come with me, you know. He said his work wasn't done there— whatever that meant."

Nicholas smiled. "Tell me about Starosta and Klaus."

Phillip took a deep breath. "Larry Starosta was my father's best friend. Both knew what it was like to go hungry and they vowed to change things for people, especially children. Grew up together and dreamt of changing the world, one child at a time. They traveled from city to city, promising a better tomorrow they couldn't follow through on."

Lula shook her head. "What happened?"

"Our father discovered the map in an old family trunk. They wanted to create their own island of hope and security to those less fortunate. But before they could, Starosta came down with the flu and never recovered. My father fell ill shortly after."

"I'm so sorry," Lula whispered. "Such a wonderful legacy though, to be so selfless."

Phillip smiled, but it didn't reach his eyes.

"Did Starosta have family?" Nicholas wasn't sure he wanted to know.

"I believe so. A daughter, I think. Mary or something like that?" Phillip scratched the back of his head while thinking. "Didn't see her much."

"Miriam?" Nicholas asked, softly.

Phillip glanced up and searched his eyes. "Yeah, that sounds right."

Nicholas sighed, confused by the connection. "Miriam was my mother," he admitted.

Phillip sat back, surprised. "So how did the grandson of Starosta get brought up by a son of Klaus?"

Nicholas's bright blue eyes met Phillip's dark gaze and his voice shook as he struggled to find the words. "I . . . I don't know."

Phillip glanced to where Marek sat silently. "Ms. Lula, three doors down is my room. You'll find an assortment of dried fruit if the boy would like to have some."

Lula's eyes filled with sympathy toward her husband. She knew Nicholas didn't need an audience. "Of course. Come, Marek."

As soon as the door clicked shut, Nicholas deflated and tears ran down his cheeks.

"A man can only be strong for everyone else for so long." Phillip grunted. "I believe it's time for you to let loose some of that load."

Tears stung his eyes and his nose burned from the effort of holding back. "I don't know how. All I want is to protect my family and make a better life for those in need. I don't want to end up like my grandfather—chasing a dream while my own child dies alone and afraid."

"You're not that man, Nicholas."

Nicholas scoffed. "How do you know?"

"Because the first thing you told me is that you want to protect your family. They came first. Larry Starosta was a good man, but he did not have his priorities in order. I know —I've read through his diaries."

Nicholas clenched his jaw. "Did you know we were almost lost at sea on our journey to Magisfjell? Then, I could've drowned this morning if it weren't for you. As right as this feels, maybe I shouldn't be here. Why else would it be this difficult?"

"You remind me so much of my son, Brian." Phillip smiled, lovingly. "I have to remind him, too."

"Remind him of what?" Nicholas asked.

"Peace is not the absence of strife. It's the presence of God in the midst of suffering—big difference."

"I don't feel worthy of God," Nicholas admitted.

"You're an admirable young man, born to lead. Maybe finish the work your grandfather always dreamt of. All I know is that our lives are intertwined and it must be for a reason. God says you're worthy. Who are you to say otherwise?"

Phillip moved closer, demanding Nicholas's attention. "Forgive 'em. Forgive your grandfather for not putting his family first. Forgive your Ma or Pa or whoever else has let you down. Let it all go and feel God in your life. Revel in this journey the Lord has brought you on. You do that—nothing will stop you."

Nicholas closed his eyes, mourning the heartache and loss his family had gone through. The desire in Larry Starosta's heart to save others, the longing inside Miriam for her husband and child, and the guilt Tomek carried for his failures.

He forgave himself for running away from Berta, for leaving Lula in Dalbeca with Mr. Brunon, and for putting Alius's life at risk in the sea. He forgave himself for not being there with Eulas when he took his last breath—for not telling him he was a greater man than Nicholas would ever be.

Then, it was gradually replaced by peace—a thankfulness for his family and the time God gave him with Eulas. Gratefulness for Phillip's presence.

Nicholas prayed for the Lord's blessing on his days to come, to reach the hearts of others with joy and giving, but most of all to be the husband and father his family needed.

He asked God to use him.

Save him.

All at once, a vision of himself appeared, surrounded by hungry and half-clothed children. Men and women came together to celebrate the birth of Christ by giving to the less fortunate—by taking care of the ones who were broken and distressed. His own children clung to the hem of his coat with the desire to be bigger than themselves, to have a small part in changing someone's life, just like their father.

This vision was meant to be.

Nicholas opened his eyes with more clarity than he'd ever felt before.

"There it is." Phillip whispered. "Nothing like the light of Christ shining through one of His own, Son."

"I don't know how to do this."

"Something tells me you'll figure it out. You aren't alone —never have been. This isn't a journey, Nicholas. It's a ministry."

"I've fought to make sense of everything since Eulas passed. I'm so grateful you're here."

Phillip smiled. "Me too. Since my father died, I've struggled with how to continue his legacy." He shook his head. "I refused to believe he died in vain. Thank you for giving me this—helping me finish their work."

"Phillip? What's kept you here all these years?"

"I guess . . . I guess I was waiting for you."

Nicholas gave a half-grin and looked down toward the floor.

"My wife, Connie, takes care of our home in Germany and I travel back and forth, charting boats every couple of weeks. She stays busy with our two grandsons, Roman and Isaac." Phillip shook his head. "I never understood what kept me coming back until now. I guess my work wasn't done either."

The magic of the Lord's will amazed Nicholas and he sat in awe of finally understanding his place in this world.

His purpose.

"Wait here. I have something for you." Phillip left the

room and quickly came back with a small, red velvet draw-string bag. "Eulas would want you to have this."

"I'm honored." Nicholas gripped the bag and nodded. "Also, I want you to know I'm sorry. I should have tried to reach you to tell you he had passed. It all happened so quickly."

Phillip's brows raised in confusion. "Son, I'm not sure what you're on about. I was there the day my brother was laid to rest. He's buried in the cemetery beside Alma. About eight years ago, I guess."

Nicholas shook his head in confusion. "But, I—no. Phillip, Eulas only passed a few years ago."

Phillip leaned forward and he frowned. "Nicholas, when did you meet my brother?"

"He found me on the shore in Brusberg when I was thir-teen. Around eight—" Nicholas paused, his heart pounding in his chest.

"Eight years ago?" Phillip added. His eyes widened as he pointed toward Nicholas. "The boat. You washed up in the canoe, right? I remember you." Phillip chuckled. "I was heading back to Magisjfell from Eulas's service."

Nicholas shook his head, "That's not possible. Eulas took me back to his cottage. He took care of me. He helped me understand Christmas!"

Phillip's chin trembled. He turned away from Nicholas and fought to control his emotions. It took several seconds before he could speak. "I guess the Lord wasn't done with him after all." He stepped toward the door on shaky legs, as if needing time alone. "You need to get some rest. Let me know if you need anything." He closed the door behind him.

Nicholas clutched the bag in his hands. He stared at the door in a daze, going over every detail—small and large. His eyes traveled over the bag and he jolted from his stupor, scrambling to pull the drawstring open. As soon as he delved inside, his hand wrapped around two objects and his vision blurred, knowing what he held. Nicholas fell to his knees in tears as he pulled out the silk red scarf and pocket watch Eulas held dear.

The same ones he'd cherished.

Lula eased the door open, her big brown eyes filled with concern. "Is everything alright?"

Nicholas smiled through tears.

"Perfect. Like Christmas morning."

EPILOGUE

25 YEARS LATER

*N*icholas Klaus chuckled as he stood by the large window overlooking Magisfjell. Marek, his oldest son and deer whisperer, corralled the reindeer in front of the sled to haul the monthly load to the dock. Ru stood in front, leading the charge, his bright pink nose gleaming in the midday sun.

Watching the herd of deer leap forward anxiously was always a sight to behold on the thick mounds of snow. They hung suspended as they jumped from hill to hill as if flying toward their destination. Their purpose.

Benson and George's boats sat waiting, the crew eager to escape the harsh winter conditions of the North. Every month they arrived to haul the handmade toys, jams and knitted clothing to surrounding countries. Magisfjell wasn't the only facility, but the biggest by far.

It had taken years for the movement to spread, but when churches and orphanages around the globe got word of their Christmas Eve tradition, letters rolled in. Every Christmas, each town was responsible for delivering food and toys to the needy in their area. The Klaus family helped as much as possible, but the true success lay with the communities.

They took care of each other—just as they should.

It gave hope where there was none. It gave faith to those that had turned their backs on the meaning of Christmas. It renewed their spirit.

Nicholas glanced down at the stack of papers on his desk. He'd never forget his first letter fifteen-years ago from a child in Russia, begging for shoes for his Papa. More and more letters were delivered, some addressed to Magisfjell, Magic Mountain or his favorite—the North Pole. He continued to obsess over this boy's request for shoes until he assigned Alius's father to the task.

Kev's journey led him to a Russian shoemaker by the name of Babikov who agreed to make the boy's father a pair of reliable boots. In fact, in recent years, he'd become their go-to shoemaker for that region and his contacts began donating materials for the Christmas gifts.

Just like that, everything came together. Year after year, businesses and locals offered services to assist their neighbors and support Nicholas's vision of creating a better world.

A better tomorrow.

Kev and Alius single-handedly began a toy division on the island where they offered wood-carving lessons to orphans. Even Alius's seven daughters, his "elves" as he calls them, have begun to take over their father's duties, creating complex toys, games, and puzzles he'd never dreamt of.

"Supplies are almost ready, Dad. Do you need anything else before we send them off?"

Nicholas turned toward the doorway where Nick stood. "Mighty big haul. Does Benson have anyone to help him?"

"His kids, Webb, Becca and Reagan are managing this load. Benson decided to stay home with Staci. Sounds like he's close to retiring."

Nicholas chuckled. "Cutting the cord?"

"Sounds like it," Nick laughed. "Speaking of cutting the cord . . ."

Nicholas shook his head. "Not sure I want you to go with me again on Christmas Eve."

Nick's mouth fell open as he stepped forward. "You said it went off without a hitch—that the children loved me."

Nicholas fought a grin as he attempted a stern expression. "Oh, they loved you alright. You and your fancy red coat. What was it they called you? Oh yeah. A Saint. Saint Nick, I believe." Nicholas rolled his eyes, but couldn't hide the pride in his voice. There was nothing he wanted more than to see his passion for helping others in his own children.

Nicholas continued to tease him. "Plus, just because you were born on Christmas doesn't mean you get your way."

"That's not what Mom says," Nick replied with an all too familiar gleam in his eye.

Nicholas chuckled. "What's that on your face?"

Nick ran his palm along the scruff on his cheeks. "You don't like it? It keeps my face warm." He grinned at his father. "You should try it."

Nicholas shook his head. "Where's your mother?"

"She's with Goldie and Minna in the girl's room teaching them to knit hats."

"I'm sure Madi and Kenzie are loving that . . ." Nicholas smirked.

"Madi is mad because she wants to train with Marek, and Kenzie would rather make toys than hats. I would not want to be in that room."

Nicholas turned and crossed his arms in front of his chest. "And you? Why exactly are you lurking in my doorway? The truth."

Nick took a deep breath before meeting his father's gaze. "I want to handle my own territory this year. Alone."

Nicholas's eyes widened. "That's a big job."

"Yes, Sir. But I know how much you love going to Poland and Germany. Let me take another. Russia, Canada, England . . . I don't care. Just—trust me."

Nicholas sighed. He swallowed his fear, hating the thought of his son on his own. But he knew he had to let go eventually. "If your mother agrees, then my answer is yes."

Nick grinned and ran out the door before his father could change his mind.

Nicholas pulled his pocket watch from his trousers to check the time. Just holding the timepiece made him feel closer to Eulas—connected. He never told anyone else the truth about their time together. It was too special to share.

Eventually, he went back to Brusberg where he turned Eulas's farm over to the orphanage. In return, they agreed to ship part of the produce from the farm to Nicholas to use for Eulas's Christmas jam.

That day, he stood in front of Eulas and Alma's tombstone, just like Phillip had said. He spent years with a man that everyone else knew to be gone. An angel from God—there was no other explanation.

Nicholas needed Eulas.

They needed each other.

"Did you really tell our son he could go off on his own this year?" Lula's high-pitched voice called out from the door. She smirked, raising one brow.

Nicholas grunted as he shuffled through the mess on his desk. "You mean Saint Nick? Papa Noel? Father Christmas? Is that the son you speak of?"

She giggled. "He is good with the children, you have to admit."

Nicholas looked up from his parchments and met her eyes. "Yeah, he is."

Lula untucked the red silk scarf from around her neck. "He's going to make you proud."

"He already has. They all have."

She walked across the room, wrapping her arms around his waist. "You told me once that you wanted to change the world."

Nicholas kissed the top of her head and nodded.

"I never doubted you," she whispered. "Not for a second."

At times such as this, he wasn't sure if changing the world was his purpose, or the purpose of his own kind-spirited children. He was just grateful to be part of it all.

One day, he would tell his grandchildren the story of his journey from the small orphanage in Torek to Magisfjell, and how it all began.

The End.

Portrait of Gulas Klaus

BY: HILARY SIMMONS

Acknowledgements

Brian, Roman & Isaac Presson
Max and Mary Ella Croft
Pastor Shandy Dill
Pastor Brett Hogland
Pastor Greg Devries
Mom and Dad
Phillip and Connie Cross
Tina Dobson
Delia Lindsey
Janis Branton
Nona Stephens
Arin Hornsby
Natalie Beaird
Betsy Parks
Susan Sharp
Staci Mason
Sarah Rhodes
Anna Benson
Paulette Berryman
Dr. Roger Mardis
Kira Gamble
Hilary Simmons
Christy Rutledge
Rylee Ferguson
Tiffany Hasty
Alicja Dunavolgyi
Gavin Cross
Marie Morgan

Thank you for your guidance, support and love.

ABOUT THE AUTHOR

A.F. Presson's career in writing began with a women's fiction novel titled Blind Trust, soon followed by Broken Trust and Interference. Blind Trust was awarded Distinguished Favorite in Women's Fiction from the Independent Press Awards and also a finalist for the Annie McDonnell Book Award. Broken Trust was awarded Distinguished Favorite in Women's Fiction from the NYC Big Book Award.

Amanda, born in Chattanooga, TN, is 40 years old and resides in North Alabama with her husband Brian, and their two sons, Roman and Isaac. When she isn't writing, she is working in a local cardiac cath lab and spending time with her family. An avid fan of music and Broadway, the arts have always played a large part in her life and she embraces the opportunity to enter the world of literature.

ALSO BY A.F. PRESSON

Printed in Great Britain
by Amazon

71578557R00170